SCARFE

Line of Attack

HAMISH HAMILTON · LONDON

Designed by Craig Dodd

Published by the Penguin Group
27 Wrights Lane, London W8 5TZ, England
Viking Penguin Inc, 40 West 23rd Street, New York, New York 10010, U.S.A.
Penguin Books Australia Ltd, Ringwood, Victoria, Australia
Penguin Books Canada Ltd, 2801 John Street, Markham, Ontaria, Canada L3R 1B4
Penguin Books (N.Z.) Ltd, 182-190 Wairau Road, Auckland 10, New Zealand

Penguin Books Ltd, Registered Offices: Harmondsworth, Middlesex, England

First published in Great Britain 1988 by Hamish Hamilton Ltd

Copyright © 1988 by Gerald Scarfe

1   3   5   7   9   10   8   6   4   2

British Library Cataloguing in Publication Data

Scarfe, Gerald
    Scarfe's line of attack.
    1. English humorous cartoons – Collections from individual artists
    I. Title
    741.5'942

    ISBN 0-241-12611-8

Printed by Butler and Tanner Ltd
Frome and London

For Jane

Is Dr. Dodo still alive?

Contents

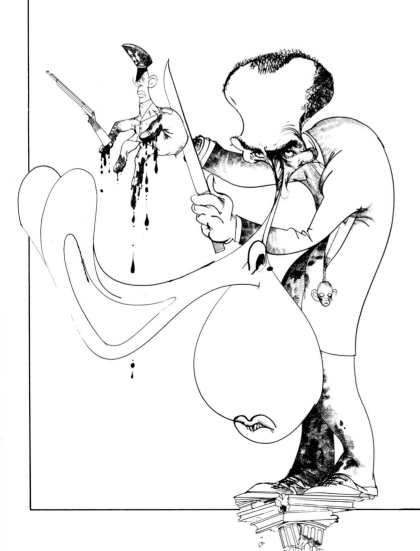

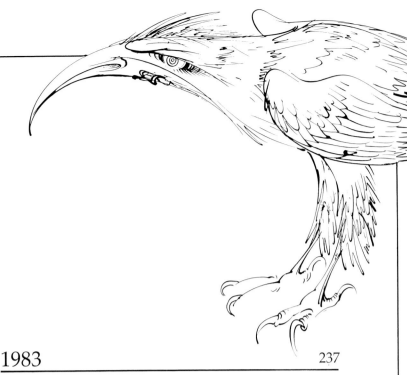

BUSH   DUKAKIS

Introduction

Deep crimson glistens on the brush he holds before him, thumb up, arm's length, measuring the naked brown-skinned girl. His palette is a spectrum of succulent ochres, vermilion, emerald green, cobalt blue, indigo and burnt umber. He lunges forward and works with feverish energy in the failing light, at one with his canvas – pausing only occasionally to throw back a glass of rough red wine from the bottle beside him. His dark-eyed nude model languorously lies midst tapestry cushions and silken drapes, her long legs carelessly arranged, watching the bearded genius before her – his paint-spattered smock; his beret. A crash of thunder and through the cracked and leaking skylight lightning illuminates the dingy garret with burning white silver. Her eyes flash with desire. . .

. . . Well, everybody knows what artists are like – I mean REAL artists – but what about cartoonists? What is a cartoonist? Is he a man screaming with laughter rolling around the floor of his studio? (do they have studios?) or is he a man crying with pain for the world crouched in a corner of his lonely room? Does he wear a smock? He probably drinks – he'd need to drink to see the funny side of life. On the other hand he wouldn't need a model unless it was Sir Geoffrey Howe. A nude Sir Geoffrey on a podium . . . no, that can't be right.

What is a cartoonist? As I lie in the scorching Italian sun beside this swimming pool in Southern Italy, it's difficult to remember. It's difficult to remember driving to the *Sunday Times* in thin drizzle, the cartoon, a sheet of white cartridge paper covered in a mass of still wet and shiny crawling black lines, lying on the back seat. Difficult to remember answers to all the questions I've been asked so often: how do you get your ideas? do you see people as you draw them? do your victims ever react? why are your drawings so grotesque? do you see anything as beautiful? what kind of drug are you on? (Campari and soda at the moment. . .)

Cartoonists are mavericks in the art world. They fit in uncomfortably if at all. They are part artist, part journalist, making weekly comments and judgements on their environment. They are not regarded as real artists: one only has to go to a Chelsea house to see how the real art is hung in the drawing room and the cartoons are hung in the lavatory. "Really frightfully amusing. You must go and have a look next time you're in the loo."

The word cartoon itself is very confusing. It can span from the ridiculous man with a big nose and stubble sitting on a desert island to the sublime drawings of Daumier who was spurned in his lifetime as a mere cartoonist but whose drawings and paintings now hang in museums all over the world.

Meanwhile, here in Italy, a cadmium-coloured butterfly dances amongst the purple bougainvillaea that tumbles over the dry stone wall. If only I could net my visions like butterflies and mount them on paper before they disappear. It's difficult to transfer ideas to paper; like the butterflies they seem exquisite when they are free in the air, but once nailed in position they lose their magic possibilities. Visions dissolve and disappear like dreams in the telling when made concrete.

Standing at the drawing board in my studio, about to pin my butterfly to paper, I dip the steel pen nib into a tiny bottle welded to a plate by years of congealed black ink. Now the moment of capture: the moment of commitment; half looking at the paper, and half hanging on to my vision, I place the point of the loaded nib onto the paper and make that first mark; like the laying of a foundation stone it commits to the shape of the final creation, and within a split second I can tell whether the drawing will work or not. I may abandon a drawing with only one line completed, because I feel it is in the wrong place, and I can see what, now committed, the line will lead onto. Each successive line bears the same danger – it may wreck the drawing as each added card on a house of cards. Every time I re-start, my vision becomes more faint until, after many false beginnings, it has disappeared, and I am merely repeating the previous mistakes. Then I must begin again with a new idea, or re-think and draw the same picture from a different angle. Sometimes, even if the line is in the wrong place, I feel I can go on and fight and wrestle it into place. Lost in a wilderness, a deep forest of sticky black lines, I can sometimes emerge triumphant.

A tiny, bright green lizard darts up the wall and stops, clinging vertically. He reminds me of Sir Alec Douglas-Home. Although not bright green Sir Alec's reptilian tongue flickered in and out and licked the thin bloodless lips of his skull-like head as he clung to the pitted wall of politics. He eventually fell off – they all do. . .

I get a particular satisfaction from drawing politicians as animals; it can be boring drawing the same people time after time. I saw Wilson as a crafty old warty toad, puffing and swelling with self-congratulatory pleasure. Callaghan was a sly old pig, snuffling and snouting for truffles in the political sty. Thatcher was a pterodactyl, razor-sharp beak, wheeling on leathery wings through a yellow prehistoric sky, swooping low on her victims with blood-red talons. Ian Smith was the almost-extinct white rhinoceros. Enoch Powell the hound of the Baskervilles, baying for immigrants' blood. Dr. David Owen, once the strutting peacock, now the dodo – is he still alive? Edward Heath as a stupid, fat stork. Nixon was the old rogue Republican elephant, a sad, sagging leather sack, hung on whitened bones, bleached in the heat of the Watergate sun. He had gone to die in the elephants' graveyard.

I suppose I was obsessed with Nixon. As I drew him time and time again, he began to transform himself. Slowly but surely his pendulant jowls began to detach themselves from the upper part of his face just below the cheekbones, and almost imperceptibly began to slide down and along his nose, releasing the rest of his face to balance at the top, and either side, of his big-dipper nose. His shoulders bowed even more, and pulled his body backwards into a huge question mark.

I have made a drawing of Mrs Thatcher (on the right), showing how this kind of progression from a more realistic impression to the abstract can take place. This is not an illustration of my mental

process, not the process I consciously go through every time I start a drawing, but more of a simple illustration of the stages I *may* go through when distilling a personality over a period of hours or weeks.

Some characters suggest their caricature immediately, others seem to have no features at all worthy of caricature. In a way, these are the more interesting, because they're a harder nut to crack. I know ultimately everybody is caricaturable, and whatever arrangement a cartoonist arrives at with his readers he can lead them to know that a triangle with spots on represents Neil Kinnock. I remember, when Ted Heath was first elected leader of the Conservative party, no one knew anything about him, outside political circles. Who was he? (hence the drawing opposite). But soon, especially once he became Prime Minister, because of his position of power, events began to influence his public persona, and I could draw him as his boat *Morning Cloud*, as Concorde or as a cracked egg, still leaving, I hope, the reader in no doubt as to who it was.

Although I can make drawings from television and newspaper pictures, I prefer to stalk my victims in the plushy glades of their natural habitats: the House of Commons, the political party conferences and on their campaign planes in America. I am a graphic paparazzo, sketching under the dinner table, in the margin of a newspaper I am apparently reading, or perhaps blindly on a piece of paper in my jacket pocket. I then take these sketches home and re-draw and interpret them in my studio, adding all the bits and pieces from the sketches to make one caricature. Only by seeing them first-hand can I tell the true character – they are always broader, shorter or fatter than you think when you seem them in real life. Colour can help; the florid face, even when drawn in black and white, helps to tell of the true character. There is something about the way they move, talk, eat, drink, walk, smoke and laugh which supplies me with all the clues. Even when I'm drawing Menachem Begin as a tank, I've still got to know the man, feel the man and feed in all the facts from my mental computer, to maintain a caricature against all odds. Menachem Begin was nothing like a tank, but the difficulties of convincing the reader that he is a tank are what make the job most intriguing. I am least interested in drawings that show the man standing there with a big head in a suit; I much prefer to make a drawing which interprets the character in some way and trasmogrifies it into something else. Caricature is so much more than a big nose, big ears and a big head on a tiny body.

Outraged victims don't come up and pole-axe me to the ground. We have a healthy tradition of political cartooning in this country, and in general I believe politicians would rather be drawn as a yellow gob of phlegm hanging on a barbed-wire fence than ignored. Such is their desire for attention. When cartooned, however badly, it means they have arrived, that they are recognised. It doesn't matter to them that they are sometimes recognised for the most awful deeds. I'm sure a cartoon does not change their course at all – they don't say, "What a naughty boy I've been! Now I see the error of my ways. I shall only work for charity in future. . ."

I suppose I have become so obsessed with my interpretations of some characters that I forget

FIRST OFFICIAL PORTRAIT OF PRIME MINISTER TED WHO?

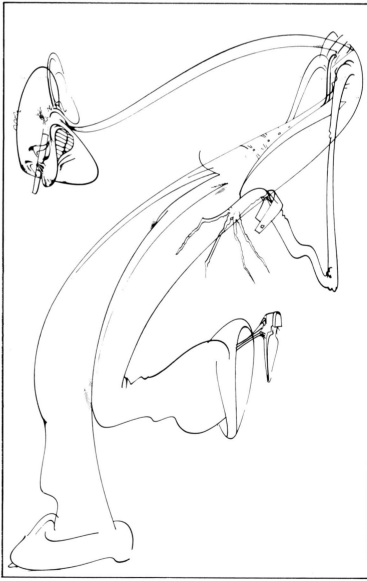

I make sketches like these of Wilson, Rippon, Home and Whitelaw at the Party Conferences. Once back in my studio these quick pencil studies bring back the character and form the basis upon which I build my caricatures.

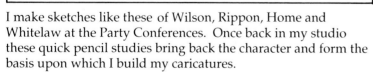

September 5 Large numbers of young school-leavers can ▶ ▶ find no work.

they are human flesh and blood. One day, walking through Victoria Station, I saw a sad little man in a neat gabardine mac, his little brown collapsed face seemed familiar, so I turned and overtook him as he crossed the forecourt, turned again, and walked towards him. It was him – it was the ogre that I had drawn so many times – the neck of a turtle with the popping eye and a swollen tongue: Ian Smith, the beast of Rhodesia. He looked lost and insignificant – could I have been wrong?

To celebrate my 21st anniversary at the *Sunday Times*, I decided to collect my political drawings in book form – a mini-history of the last 21 years. After the difficult task of choosing which drawings to include, I spent weeks poring over yellowing back editions of the *Sunday Times* trying to discover the political background to each drawing. Most bring back the moment with clarity – Biafra, Watergate, Chernobyl – but there are some where I had not only forgotten what they were about, but had forgotten I had actually drawn them. After piecing together the facts, whenever my yellowing newspaper research allowed, I have written a brief summary to print with each drawing to give a little flavour of the time.

As I put the drawings in this book together, and wrote the accompanying captions, I had a slight feeling of depression that so little has changed, despite all the sound and fury. The drawing 'Join A to B, Baffles World Leaders' of 1970 shows the effect of war and famine in Biafra. The same drawing, some 15 years later, applies to the war and famine in Ethiopia. On the other hand, who would have thought the incoming, war-mongering President Reagan (defence budget increased by 100 billion dollars) would have turned out to be the man in the '80s desperate to achieve peace with Gorbachev?

But, above all, making my drawings has taught me that the big and little tin-pot generals come and go; people continue to be slaughtered and starved and used as cannon-fodder. It is the misuse of power, from the smallest, crookedest local councillor to the biggest, bloodiest Stalin, that fires my political drawings.

Castellabate, August 1988.

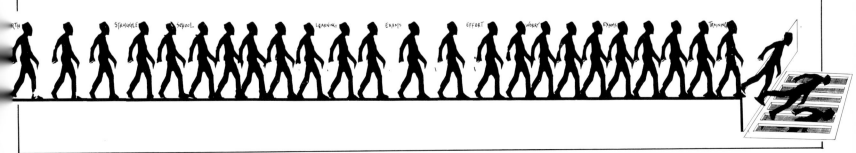

TWENTY-FIVE YEARS
OF DRAWINGS
WHICH APPEARED IN
THE SUNDAY TIMES

1967

Conférence de Presse du Général de Gaulle – Palais de L'Élysée – Paris

May 21 President de Gaulle in the Elysée Palace, Paris - a drawing I made from life on the spot. The experience was like an audience with God. In 1963 President de Gaulle had vetoed Britain's entry into the Common Market. Pompidou, in the corner, is to succeed him as President of France. Wilson is in the palm of his hand.

◀ **July 30** Race riots in America - Black Power calls for guerilla war against the whites.

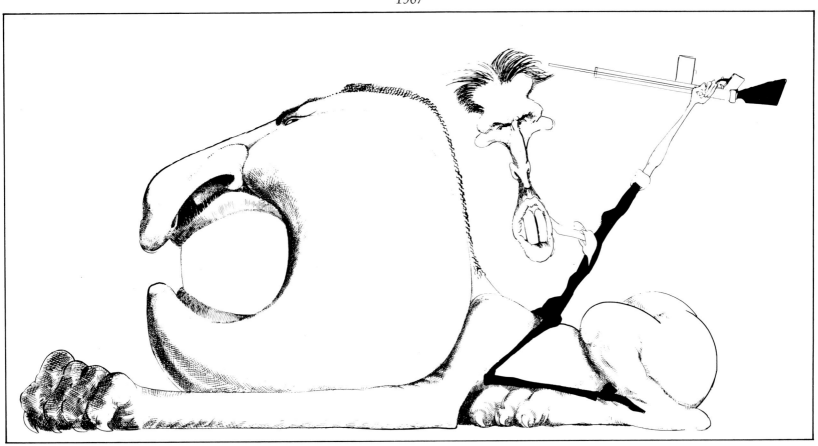

August 6 Houari Boumedienne of Algeria challenges President Nasser of Egypt for the Arab leadership

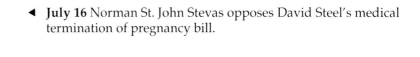

◀ **July 16** Norman St. John Stevas opposes David Steel's medical termination of pregnancy bill.

December 24 The Drunken Driver.

1968

March 24 Hawk General Westmoreland is recalled from Vietnam by Johnson in an effort to improve his Presidential image. America is puzzled. How is a small country like North Vietnam capable of resisting the technical superiority of US weapons? At the same time America is under strain with the racial crisis.

◀ **July 14** Hubert Humphrey's dilemma in his race for the White House. If he echoes Johnson he loses essential votes: if he goes on his own he loses President LBJ's backing, essential for the nomination.

Drawing made to advertise *The Times*. President Johnson tries to ▶ rise from the unpopularity of the engulfing war in Vietnam which gathers momentum as more and more young soldiers are drafted.

The Primaries. Drawing made in Los Angeles in June and printed in the *Sunday Times* on August 4. The candidates are: the charismatic Robert Kennedy (with his dog Freckles), Eugene McCarthy, the man who made opposition to the Vietnam War respectable, Richard Nixon, who lost against John Kennedy in 1960. Governor Ronald Reagan of California hovers in the background.

Robert Kennedy is assassinated in June at the Ambassador's Hotel, Los Angeles.

December 20 President Johnson is forced from the Presidential race by inflation, the welfare programme, violence and crime and, above all, by the divisive Vietnam War at the end of his era. Richard Nixon eventually becomes President.

1969

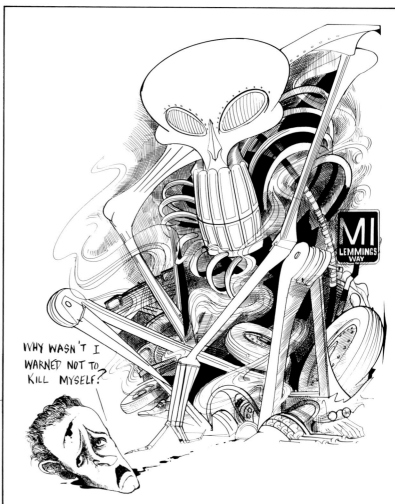

December 7 President Pompidou of France invites Prime Minister Harold Wilson into the Common Market. The European Summit in The Hague decides to negotiate Britain's entry into Europe before the summer.

◄ **December 14** Civil war in Nigeria. Biafra is isolated. Wilson wishes to protect British interests and stop Nigeria turning towards Russia.

January 12 Motorway Madness. There is a series of multiple crashes on Britain's motorways.

December 26 Unable to bring down Israel, Arab guerillas threaten the stability of every Arab regime

Daddy, what did *YOU* do in the Great War?

November 30 Vietnam Soldier. Now Nixon is enmeshed in the Vietnam War and pictures of massacres by American soldiers are reaching the news stands. Nixon says, 'If I allow a Communist take-over in South Vietnam the office of President of the United States would lose respect throughout the world.'

1970

HEATH ELECTED PRIME MINISTER

It's a living

BUY ME AND STOP ONE

June 21 Wilson loses the election. Despite polls indicating a Labour victory, Edward Heath is elected Prime Minister. Enoch Powell continues to gnaw away at the issues of race and Northern Ireland.

May 12 Sir Alec Douglas-Home, Foreign Secretary, as an arms salesman.

May 31 Wilson and Heath. 'Mirror Mirror, if you can, show me now an honest man.' There have been six years of Labour government. Judging the time and polls to be right, the Prime Minister and great showman Harold Wilson calls an election for June 19. He loses.

June 28 The Arts Council: Lord Eccles is made Arts Minister, Lord Goodman and Jenny Lee look on.

A COMMON MARKETEER

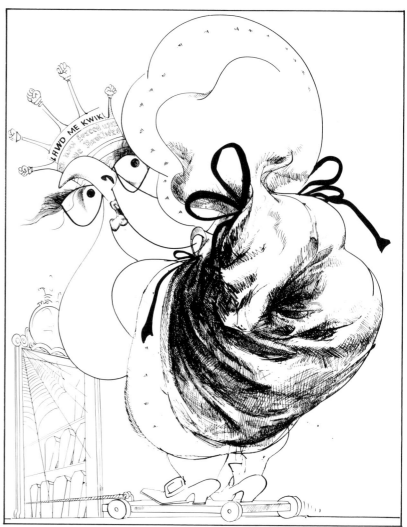

July 5 Anthony Barber, Minister with special responsibility for Europe.

August 23 George Brown, our one-time colourful Foreign Secretary, is wheeled into the Lords.

June 7 Enoch Powell as a skinhead. His racist attacks inspired me ▶ to more and more grotesqueries. In 1968 he made a speech in Birmingham, warning about immigrants, 'As I look ahead I am filled with foreboding. Like the Romans I seem to see the River Tiber foaming with much blood.'

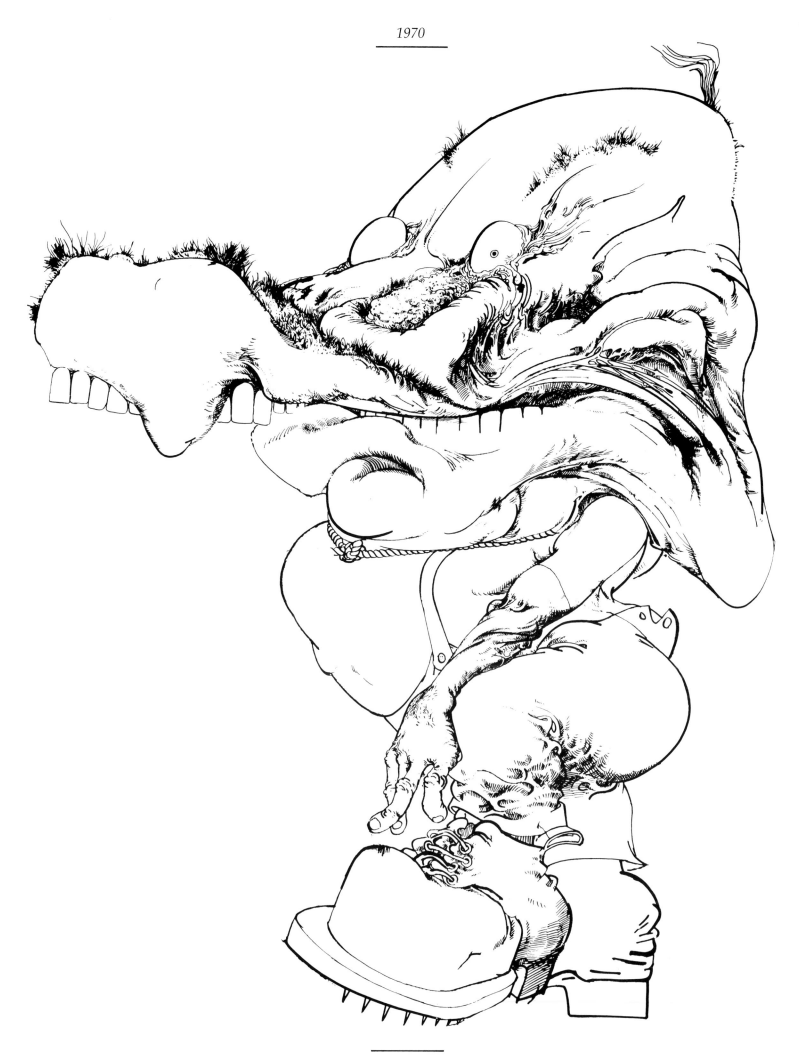

June 25 Biafra. Terrible famine caused by the war in Biafra.

July 5 Big arms haul in the Falls Road, Northern Ireland

August 9 President Nixon drops a casual remark in the middle of a political speech, pre-judging the guilt of the Charles Manson gang who murdered a houseful of people in Los Angeles. **August 16** Pollution ▶

WOMENS LIBERATION FRONT   OR   VENUS RISES

August 30 Women's Liberation

November 15 Ian Smith continues his oppression in Rhodesia.

September 13 Four jet liners and 594 passengers are hi-jacked by Palestinian terrorists at Dawson's field in Jordan. They want the release of Leila Khaled from Ealing police station

September 20 Israel, in the person of General Dayan, looks on as Arab fights Arab.

December 6 President Nasser of Egypt and General Dayan of Israel

October 11 The new Prime Minister Edward Heath and his Cabinet, with behind him Sir Alec Douglas-Home and before him William Whitelaw, Anthony Barber, Robert Carr, Peter Walker, Reginald Maudling, Sir Keith Joseph, Geoffrey Rippon and, appearing for the first time, Margaret Thatcher.

November 8 A poster for the Conservative Party, inspired by a Tory poster calling Labour Yesterday's Men. 'The Day Before Yesterday's Men', shows Prime Minister Edward Heath, Sir Alec Douglas-Home, Anthony Barber, John Davies and Robert Carr.

November 22 Terrible floods in East Pakistan: aid comes to victims too late. The Red Cross announce that they are postponing further air shipments to East Pakistan because of the pile-up of supplies in Dacca. The death toll in the Bay of Bengal is put at 166,000 but expected to rise to one million.

1971

January 17 Clockwork Prime Minister Edward Heath marches relentlessly on.

January 24 Edward Heath is angry when the Commonwealth conference in Singapore disapproves of the government selling maritime arms to South Africa

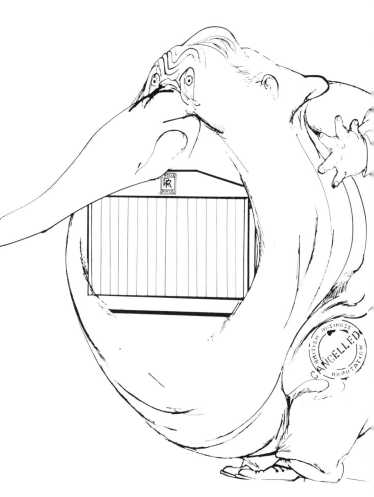

February 7 Edward Heath. The Government nationalises the aero-engine side of Rolls-Royce. Labour is cock-a-hoop about this reverse in Conservative policies.

February 14 Valentine's Day. Edward Heath and decimalisation.

February 28 Reginald Maudling, Home Secretary, and the racially discriminative Immigration Bill. Registration was required at police stations. There were hysterical reports that the country was being flooded with black immigrants. Enoch Powell's name was frequently linked with these reports.

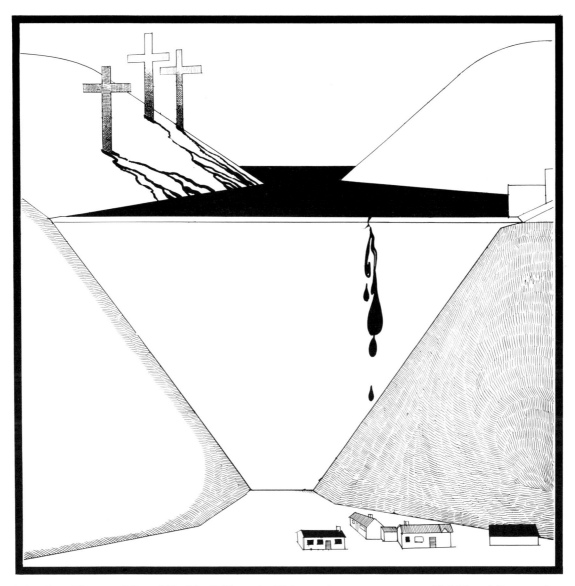

March 14 Three soldiers killed in Belfast. An IRA regular statement says 'British soldiers are here and they can expect things like this to happen.'

February 21 The Domino Theory; Nixon's election prospects for a second term of office in 1972
are harassed by the war in Vietnam despite giant troop withdrawals.

April 4 The American Sacrifice. President Nixon releases Lieutenant Calley, the leader of the My
Lai massacre in Vietnam when American soldiers shot helpless women and children. Nixon hopes this will be ▶
a popular move which will help his election chances. In July Nixon is to visit Peking.

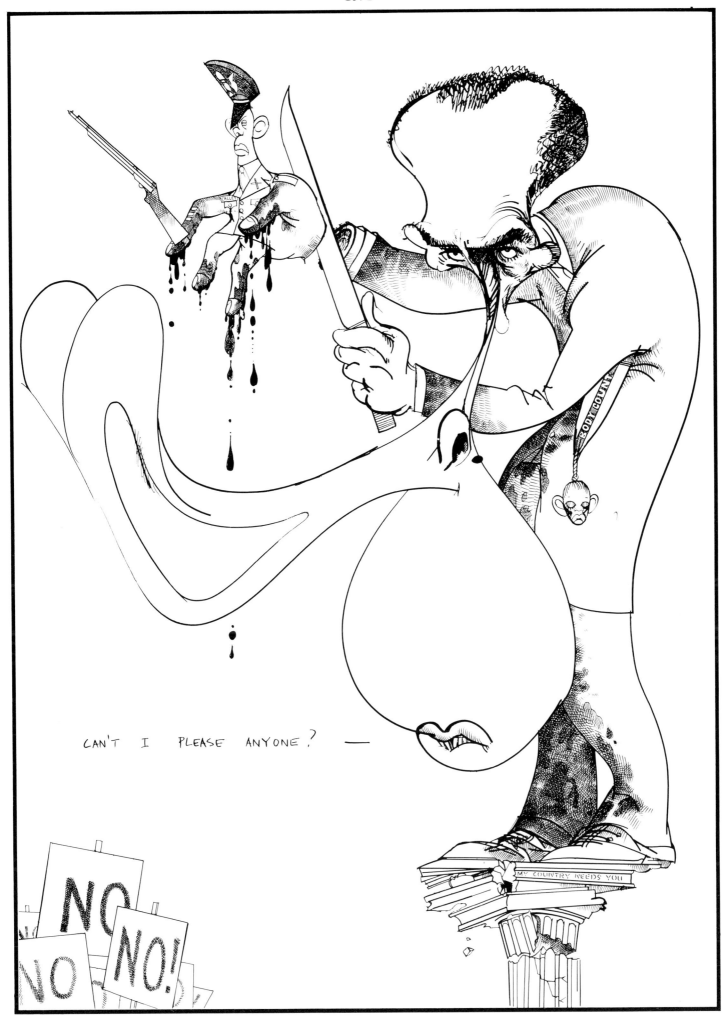

May 9 The Real Obscenity. War rages in Pakistan. President Yahya
Khan's West Pakistan army invades East Pakistan and represses
the freely elected government of Sheikh Mugib ur Rahman. The
House of Lords debates obscenity.

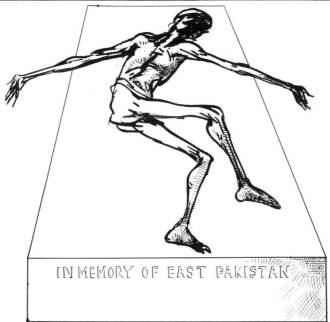

June 6 Foreign Aid comes too late for those dying of cholera in their refugee camps in India. Millions of refugees have flooded into India from Pakistan.

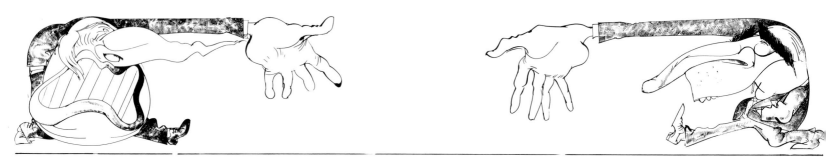

May 16 President Pompidou and Prime Minister Heath are to meet. Pompidou has always expressed his hope and conviction that Britain would enter the EEC.

June 27 Edward Heath is ecstatic about taking Britain into the EEC. He has always been a consistent European. Terms for British entry are now settled. I could hear Heath's plummy voice as I drew him. I sometimes found myself flouncing around imitating his movements to get the feel of him.

May 23 Edward Heath meets President Pompidou in Paris. It is feared Britain will come off worst when she joins the Common Market. There are difficulties over sugar, New Zealand butter, and other housekeeping details.

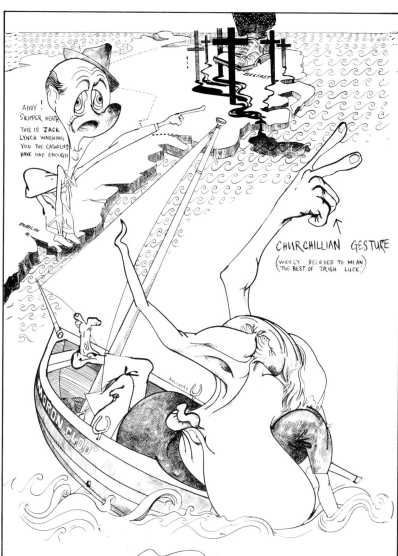

August 15 Internment: indefinite imprisonment without trial is introduced on August 9 as an instrument of justice in Northern Ireland.

August 22 The Prime Minister of Ireland, Jack Lynch, attacks Edward Heath over the Ulster internment programme. Heath frequently enjoyed relaxing on his boat '*Morning Cloud*'.

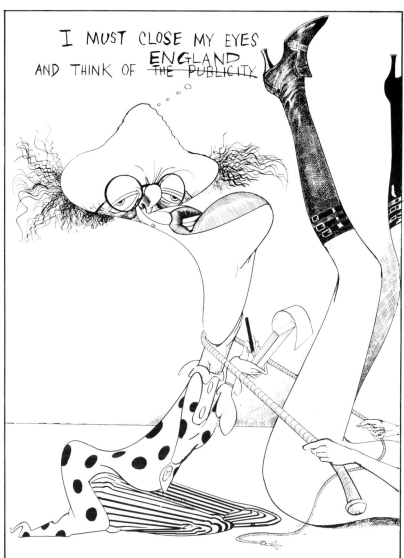

August 8 The Oz trial in which the 'school kids' issue of the underground magazine Oz was prosecuted for obscenity. Richard Neville (editor) and two others are sentenced by Judge Argyle to 16 months in prison. Mary Whitehouse dances in the background.

August 29 The obscenity debate rages on. Lord Longford heads an enquiry.

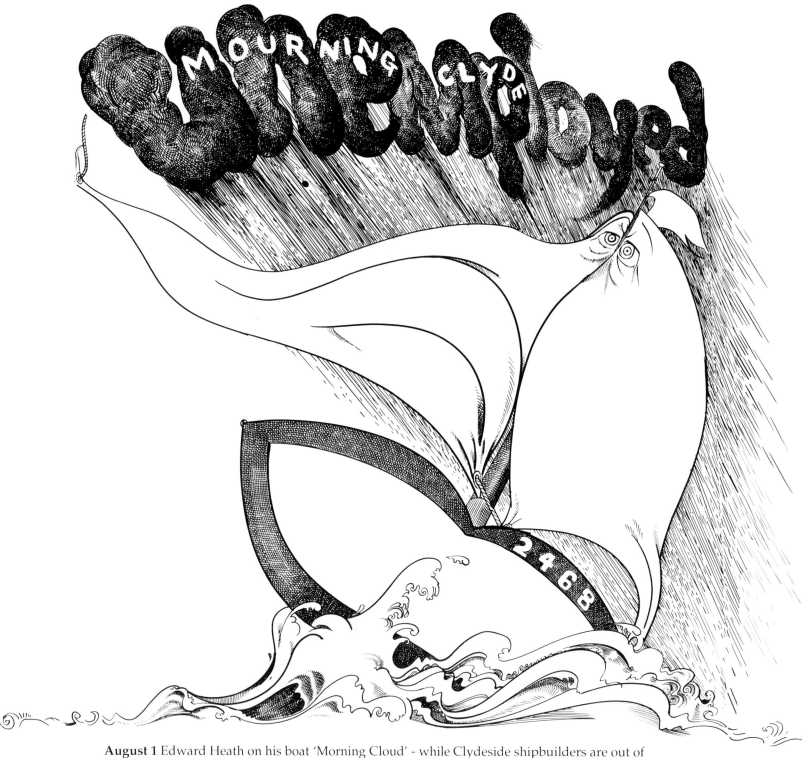

August 1 Edward Heath on his boat 'Morning Cloud' - while Clydeside shipbuilders are out of work. £20 million of public money is pumped into Upper Clyde Shipbuilders to no avail. Wedgwood Benn advocates workers' control.

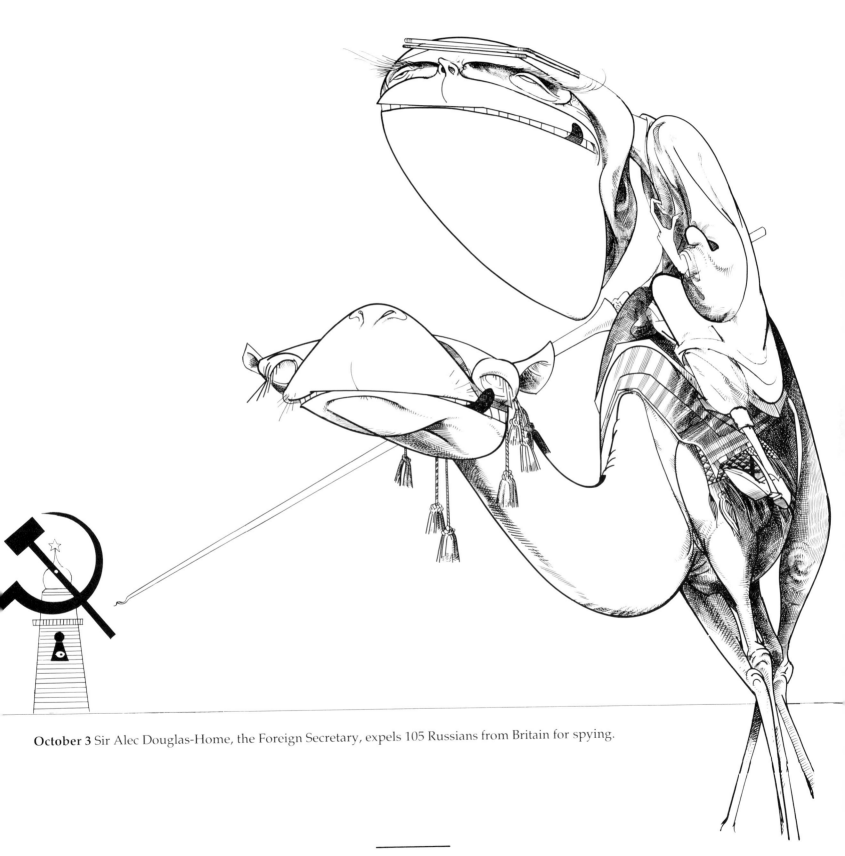

October 3 Sir Alec Douglas-Home, the Foreign Secretary, expels 105 Russians from Britain for spying.

October 10 The Labour Party Conference, Brighton: James Callaghan, Denis Healey, Anthony Wedgwood Benn, Harold Wilson and Roy Jenkins being tempted by pro-Europeans, Edward Heath, Home, Rippon and Prior. Enoch Powell as a crab nips Heath.

October 17 The Conservative Party Conference, Brighton: the government is unpopular. The economy has not taken off. Unemployment is nearly one million. Reginald Maudling, John Davies, Lord Carrington, Geoffrey Rippon, Sir Alec Douglas-Home, Anthony Barber, Robert Carr, Christopher Chataway, Edward Heath and Jim Prior.

March 7 Ted Heath, as Muhammed Ali, the boxer floors Tom Jackson, leader during the Post Office workers' strike. Vic Feather, leader of the TUC, enters the ring. Wages are rising at 14%, prices at 8%, unemployment 3 to 4 million.

1972

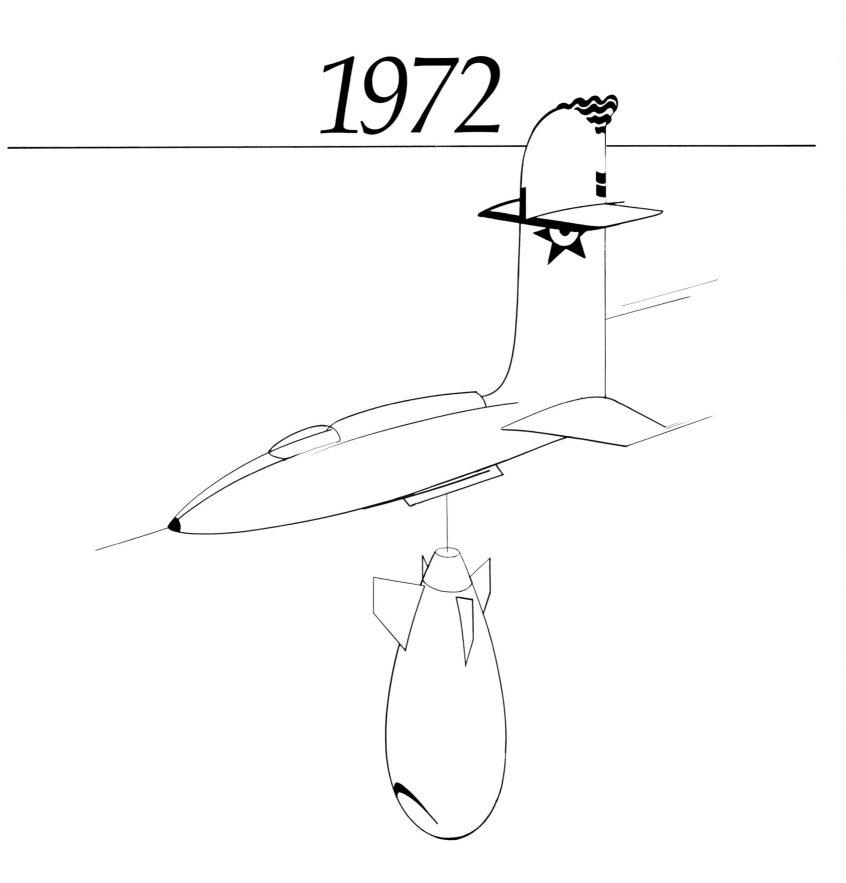

March 19 French Premier Georges Pompidou surprisingly announces to Edward Heath that he has decided to hold a nationwide referendum in France on Britain's entry into Europe. Many bitterly oppose entry but a massive 'Oui' is expected.

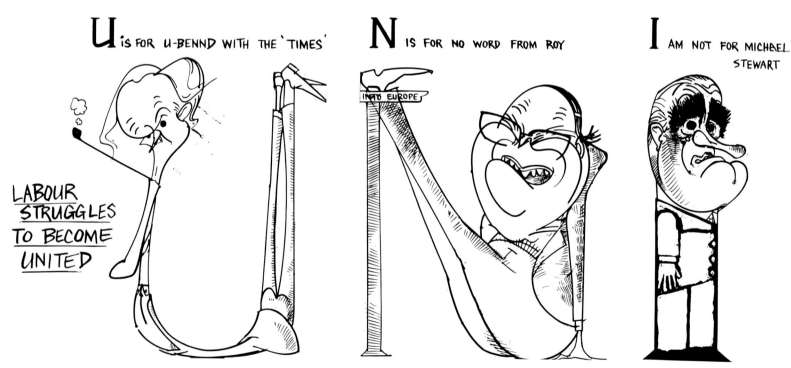

◄ **November 12** Nixon in the shape of war plane and bomb. Nixon has had a landslide re-election against Senator McGovern. About Vietnam, he says, 'Peace with honour and never peace with surrender.' A ceasefire is imminent.

April 23 The unions are reluctant to play their part in the Industrial Relations Act, but Vic Feather, General Secretary of the TUC, attempts to persuade them to attend court. Maurice Macmillan wields the whip. Sidney Weighell of the NUR agrees.

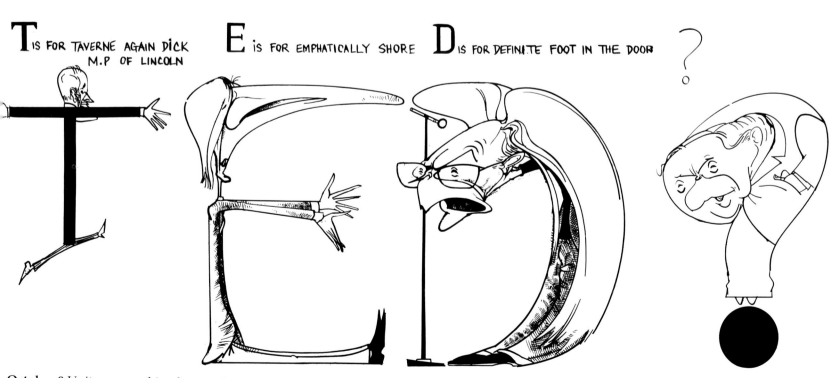

T IS FOR TAVERNE AGAIN DICK M.P OF LINCOLN   E IS FOR EMPHATICALLY SHORE   D IS FOR DEFINITE FOOT IN THE DOOR

October 8 Unity, or anything but, in the Labour Party. Callaghan, Wedgwood Benn, Roy Jenkins, Michael Stewart, Dick Taverne, Peter Shore, Michael Foot, Harold Wilson.

June 18 The Red Queen. The smell of failure and farce begins to surround the government. The Industrial Relations Court has failed to make its contempt writ stick, even after summoning up the High Court tipstaff and the official solicitor. The government's stand has been weakened by public sympathy for the dockers, whom they see as an underpaid group.

July 30 Edward Heath and the Industrial Relations Act. The Act gave individuals new rights to belong to trade unions if they wished and to be compensated for unfair dismissal; it gave unions new chances to recruit and win recognition from hostile employers; and it gave the government the opportunity to intervene in strikes that were damaging to society as a whole.

July 23 Reginald Maudling, involved in the Poulson scandal, (influence and corruption in building) resigns. Harry Hyams (builder of Centre Point), Anthony Barber, Peter Walker, Home Secretary Willie Whitelaw, enmeshed in Northern Ireland. Edward Heath tries to make the Industrial Relations Court work. However, the trade unions refuse to be registered, thus nothing to prevent the Act from working. Five dockers exploit the Act and are put in Pentonville.

A COMIC OPERA IN THREE INDUSTRIAL RELATIONS ACTS.

WHEN A DOCKER'S NOT ENGAGED IN HIS EMPLOYMENT
I MUST THEN INVENT A LAW TO GET HIM BACK,
BUT HE FACES JAIL WITH, SEEMINGLY, ENJOYMENT
AND IT LOOKS AS IF I'LL GET THE BLOODY SACK
WHEN A WORKING MAN JOINS FORCES WITH HIS BROTHER,
THE BATTLE WITH THE UNIONS CAN'T BE WON
AH, TAKE ONE CONSIDERATION WITH ANOTHER,
A PREMIER'S LOT IS NOT A HAPPY ONE!

MY OBJECT ALL SUBLIME
I SHALL ACHIEVE IN TIME,
TO MAKE THESE CRIPPLING STRIKES,
THESE CRIPPLING STRIKES A CRIME,
AND MAKE EACH DOCKER REPENT
THE PICKETING TIME HE'S SPENT
I MAY LOOK WEAK, BUT I'M
I'M WEAK, BUT I'M HEAVEN SENT,
HEAVEN SENT!

TUF TED

BOO! BOO! SSSS! SSSS!

I AM THE VERY PATTERN OF THE
OFFICI—AL SOLICITOR,
I'M CONJURED UP IMMEDIATELY
WHEN'EVER THAT I WISH IT TER,
I'VE WAYS OF GETTING ROUND IT
WHEN THAT THINGS HAVE GONE PECULIAR,
WHEN DOCKERS PUT ME IN THE DOCK,
I'LL EVEN BREAK A RULE FOR YER.

Gerald Scarfe July '72

AS YOUR P.M. I'VE SERVED SUCH A TERM,
AND OOOOOH I'VE TRIED TO BE SO FIRM,
I'VE CLEANED UP THE WORKERS AND I'VE CLEANED
UP THE IRISH
AND I'VE KNACKERED UP THE COUNTRY IN A
MANNER SQUIRE-ISH,
I'VE KNACKERED UP THE COUNTRY
SO SUCCESSFULLEE
HOW LONG WILL I BE RULER OF THE
QUEEN'S COUNTREE?

CHUCK HIM OFF!

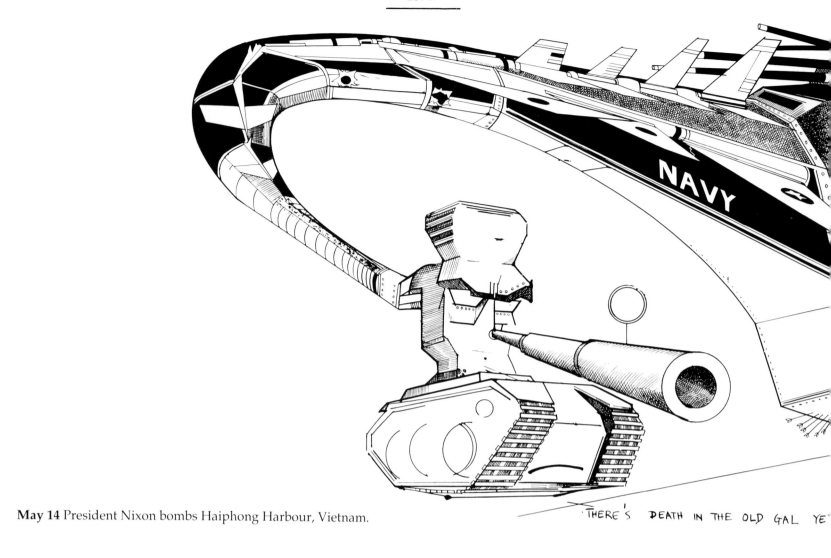

May 14 President Nixon bombs Haiphong Harbour, Vietnam.

THERE'S DEATH IN THE OLD GAL YET

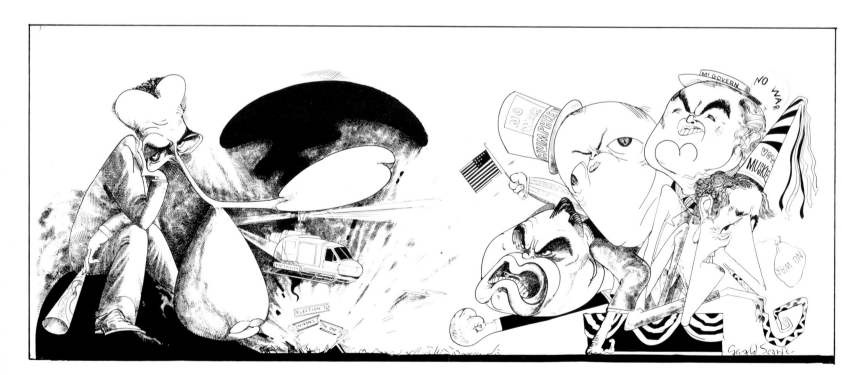

April 9 Nixon's election chances continue to be spoiled by conflict in Vietman. As the election approaches, America cannot maintain the war. Nixon has reduced American ground troups from 549,000 to 69,000 but to show that the US is not weakening he continues to bomb Hanoi and Haiphong. The other candidates are: Governor George Wallace, Senator Humphrey, Senator McGovern and Senator Muskie.

BRONTOSAURUS AMERICANUS (THOUGHT EXTINCT) LAYING EGGS.

April 30 Nixon tries to quit Vietnam as the election looms. America's might has been thwarted by the nature of the guerilla warfare in difficult terrain.

Pollution

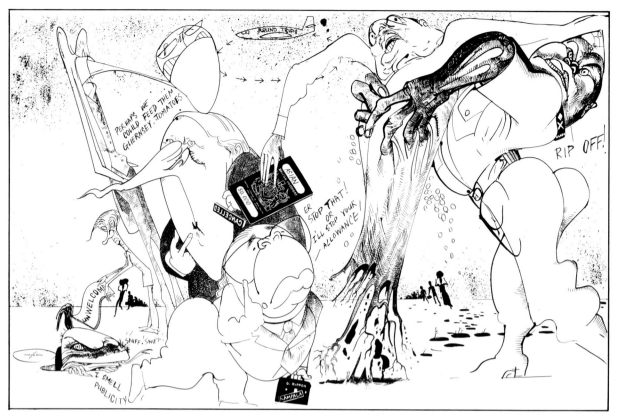

August 13 General Idi Amin uproots and throws out the Ugandan Asians, despite protestations from Geoffrey Rippon. There are 30,000 British Asians in Uganda and there is great controversy about allowing them into England, although they are British citizens. Also present Robert Carr, Alec Douglas-Home, Edward Heath and Enoch Powell.

August 20 The Olympic Games are to be held in Munich. Edward Heath, Alec Douglas-Home and some of their problems. Planeloads of Asians are arriving in England having been given 48 hours to leave Uganda.

September 24 Fire Risk. General Idi Amin threatens to enflame Africa. Amin confirms that Libyans have arrived in Uganda. Heavy fighting between Ugandan and Tanzanian troops.

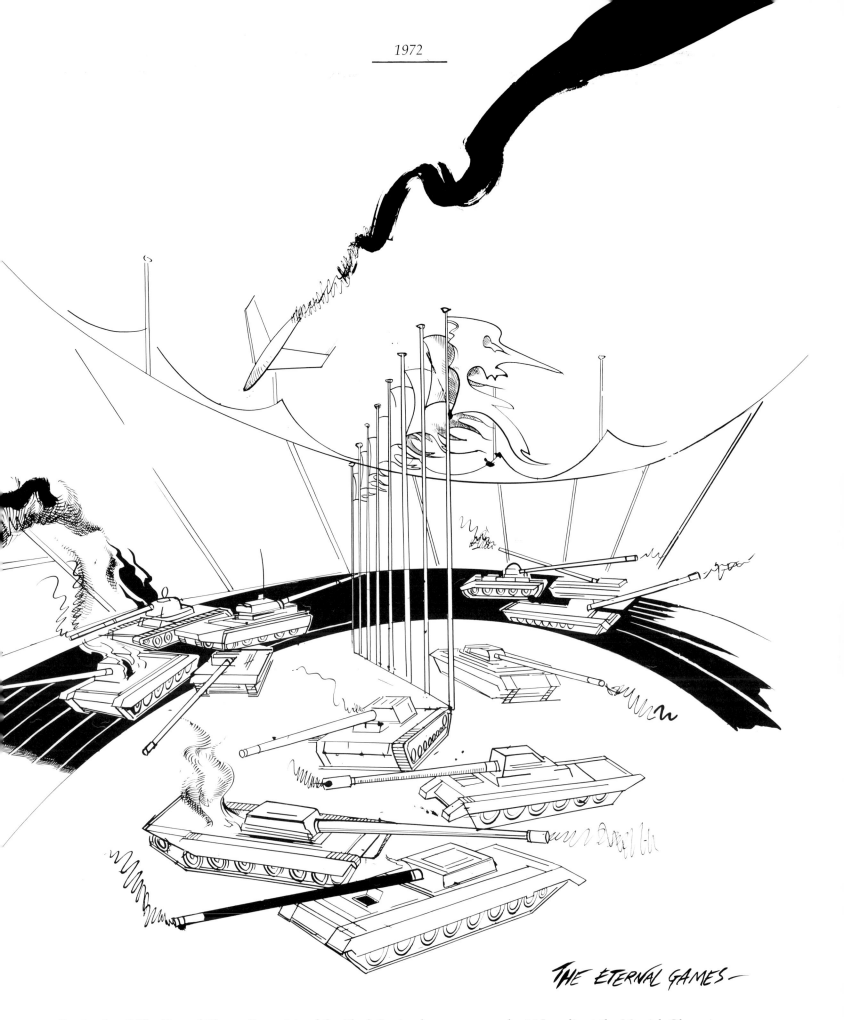

THE ETERNAL GAMES—

September 3 The Eternal Flame. Terrorists of the Black September group murder 11 Israelis at the Munich Olympics.

October 15 Two naughty seaside postcards I sent from the Conservative Party Conference, Blackpool, featuring Geoffrey Rippon, Edward Heath and the Common Market (there is talk of a referendum), Sir Alec Douglas-Home, Enoch Powell, Margaret Thatcher, and black immigration.

November 12 Alec Douglas-Home - ancient human remains found ▶ in Africa. On the shores of Lake Rudolph in Kenya the oldest hominid fossil is discovered. It is call the 1470 man and is two and a half million years old. 1470 man has a brain twice the size of Australopithecus though at least a million years older.

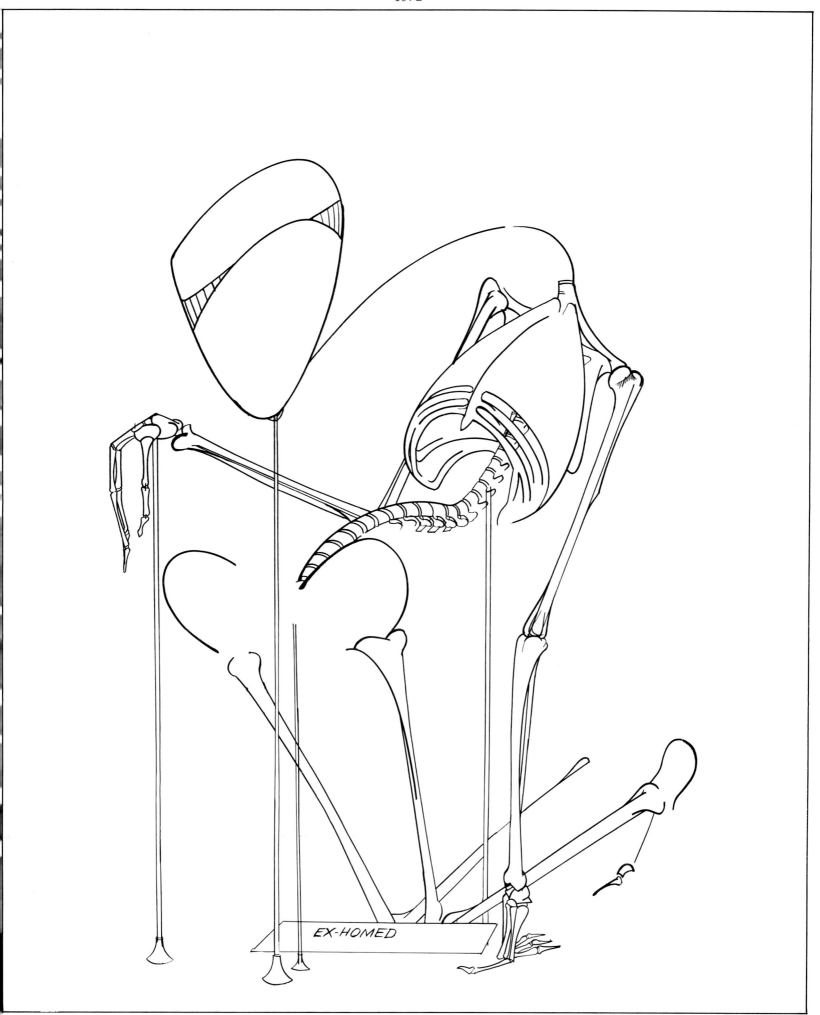

EX-HOMED

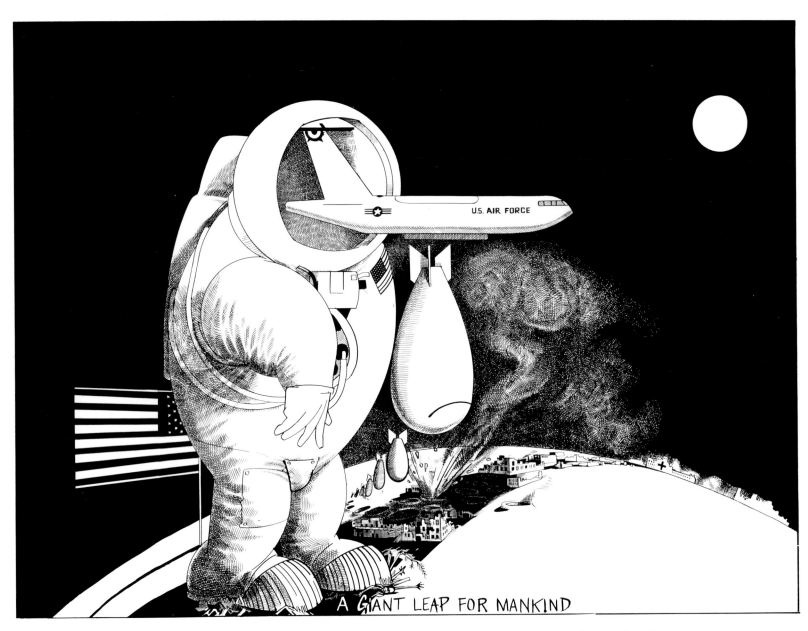

A GIANT LEAP FOR MANKIND

December 24 President Nixon (compiled from an Astronaut, Bomber and Bomb). There is a break-down of understanding in negotiations to end the war so President Nixon orders the fiercest and most devastating saturation bombing of the Hanoi-Haiphong heartland in Vietnam for Christmas. Merry Christmas.

1973

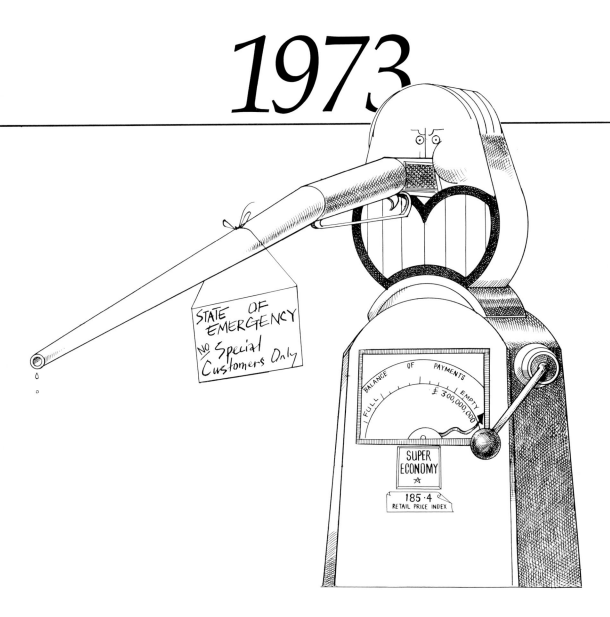

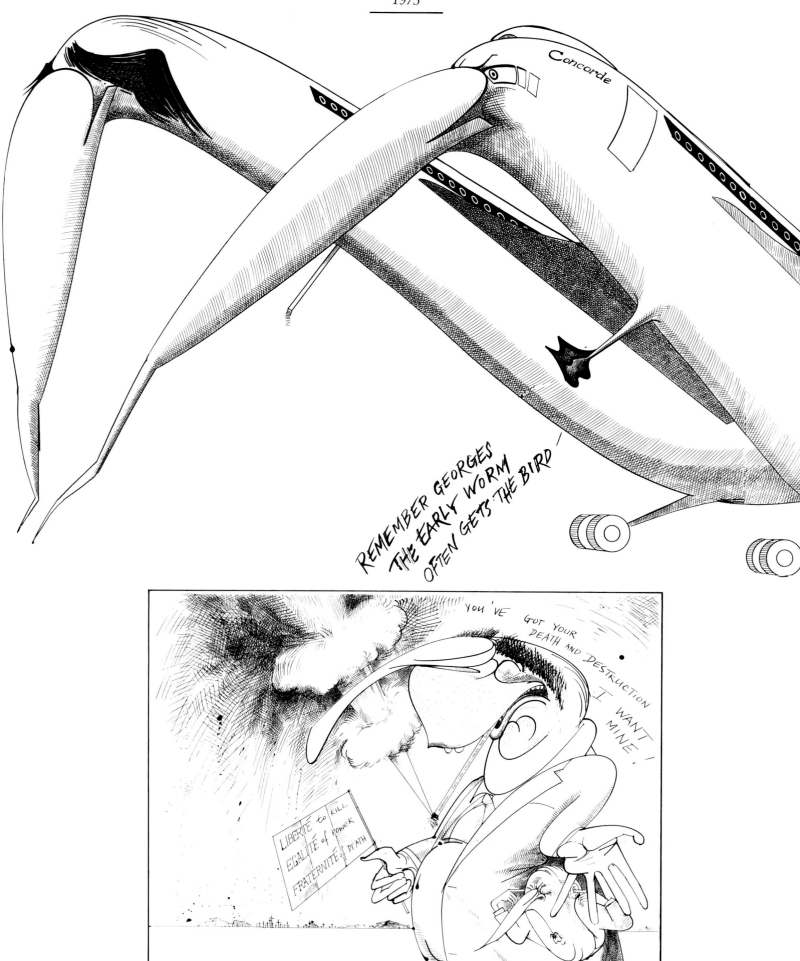

July 15 France explodes it's own atom bomb in the Pacific off Australia.
President Pompidou and Prime Minister Heath.

November 18 Petrol shortage. Record interest rates, oil and coal crisis, balance of payments shock continuing. Oil has transformed Saudi Arabia from an isolated country into a rich and influential kingdom. Saudi Arabia imposes an oil embargo as a political weapon aimed at the US in the hope that Nixon will coax the Israelis into an unfavourable settlement in the Middle East.

February 4 'Entente Concordes'. President Georges Pompidou and Prime Minister Edward Heath as Concordes. £62 million has been committed by Britain to develop the supersonic Concorde with a further £215 million needed. Calls are heard to halt this joint Anglo-French project. Hopes that American companies TWA and Pan Am would take Concorde seem doubtful. Cancellation would harm Anglo-French relations.

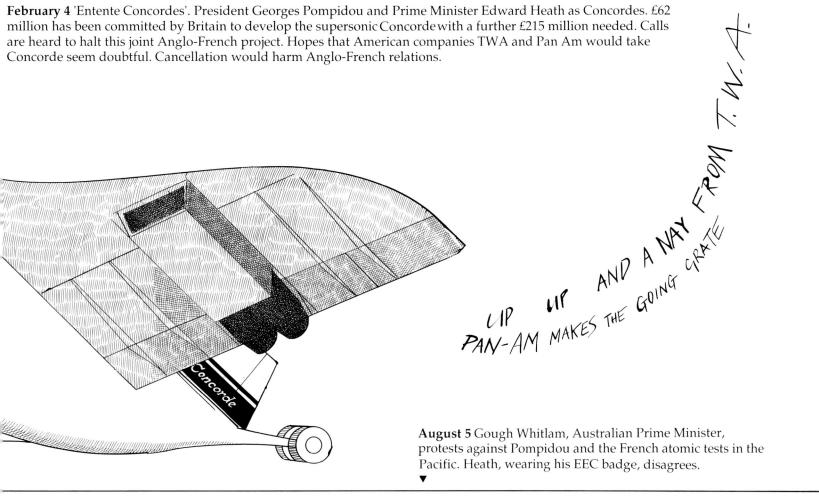

August 5 Gough Whitlam, Australian Prime Minister, protests against Pompidou and the French atomic tests in the Pacific. Heath, wearing his EEC badge, disagrees.

February 25 Israel shoots down a Libyan commercial airliner with the loss of 106 lives, after it strays into their air space. General Dayan.

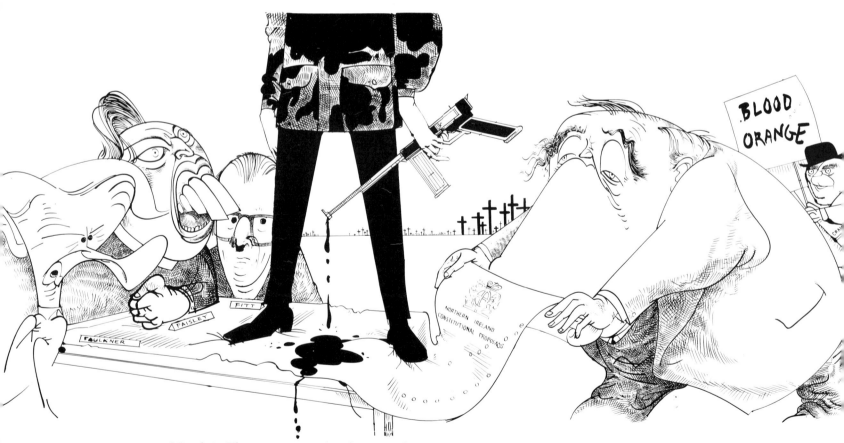

March 25 The government produces a White Paper on Northern Ireland, proposing to rebuild the north's political institutions so that the minority, the Catholics, can have a guaranteed share in government. Prime Minister Faulkner, The Rev. Ian Paisley, Gerry Fitt and Home Secretary William Whitelaw.

April 1 VAT is introduced by Anthony Barber, Chancellor of the Exchequer.
A comprehensive revision of the tax system.

April 15 European Butter Mountain. Edward Heath as the symbol for Stork Margarine. As much butter as Britain consumes every year is stored in European warehouses and when about to go bad is sold to Russia at 8p a pound (British grocers pay 25p). The British have contributed £12 million to the cost of butter production. It can't be sold cheaply to Britain because she is a member of the Common Market and that would undermine the system, so the Russians benefit from Common Market Policy food price scheme.

April 23 Easter Parade of 1973 worthies:

Tories - Home, Godber, Thatcher, Whitelaw, Heath, Rippon, Barber, Powell as horse.

Labour - Healey, Callaghan, Wilson, Jenkins, Benn.

Unions - Vic Feather, Hugh Scanlon, Jack Jones, Tom Jackson, Sid Weighell, Joe Gormley, Clive Jenkins.

EVERYTHING IN THE GARDEN IS LOVELY

May 27 Something nasty in the woodshed: Heath carries on optimistically despite several problems. He achieves an economic breakthrough and the election is 18 months away. In additon to the scandal of Poulson and Lonrho and the problem of Northern Ireland, compromising photographs of Lord Lambton and the prostitute Norma Levy are touted round the newspapers. There is an immediate scare about security leaks. Lambton resigns. Lord Jellicoe, Leader of the House of Lords, is also implicated.

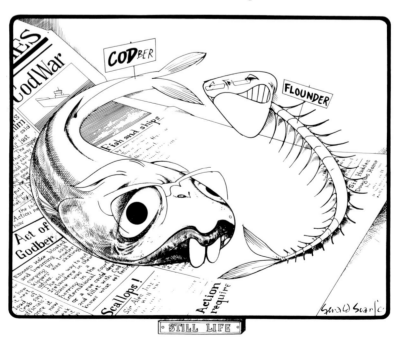

STILL LIFE

May 20 Iceland proclaims a 50 mile fishing limit. The Royal Navy is sent to protect British trawlers fishing, as they always have done, 25 miles inside this area. Minister of Agriculture and Fisheries Joseph Godber and Foreign Secretary Home

July 1 Ian Smith and Sir Alec Douglas-Home. There is an eclipse of the sun in Africa as Lord Home, aged 70, carries on with negotiations.

July 29 Table de Vote: The Liberals show that they are an electoral force when Clement Freud (well-known gastronome) wins the Isle of Ely. Liberal leader Jeremy Thorpe, Heath and Clement Freud. Harold Wilson as pie.

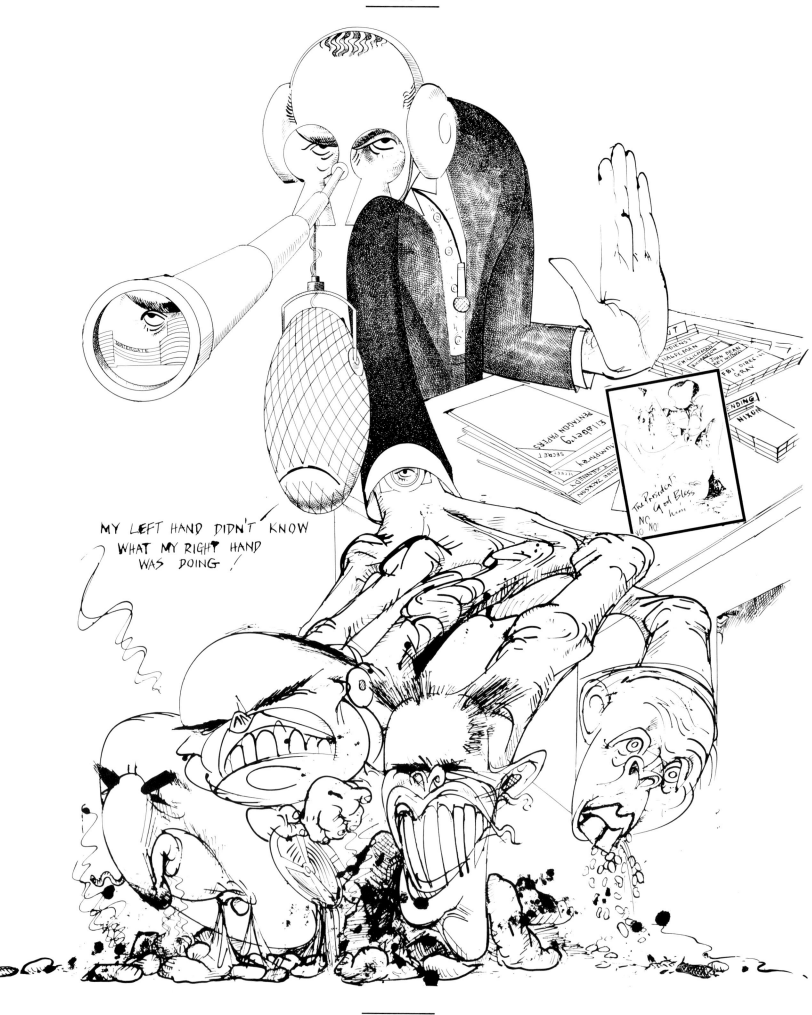

◄ **May 6** Nixon says he doesn't know about Watergate, the name given to a White House-inspired web of wire taps, burglaries, bribery, lies and forgery. Senator McGovern has emerged as a stronger runner than the Republicans could have wished. The Committee for the re-election of the President (better known as CREEP) breaks into the offices of McGovern's headquarters in the Watergate building, Washington. Nixon denies any knowledge, but former White House lawyer John Dean says he is ready to testify that Nixon twice joined his aids in a cover-up operation. Top Presidential aids Ehrlichman and Haldeman have resigned.

August 19 Watergate. The net closes in on Nixon. The Senate is now investigating Watergate, and Nixon is witholding forbidden tapes. The President says he did not know what happened, but refuses to give the Senate tape recordings which would prove whether he did or did not know about Watergate. Impeachment has reared its ugly head. He appears on television to ask the nation to accept his innocence but does not rebut the charges against him. He is banking on the hope that the public is suffering from an overdose of Watergate.

November 11 Henry Kissinger, Nixon's flying diplomat, visits the Middle East Egypt as the Watergate scandal gathers momentum

THE AMAZING JADED MAN

THIS WEEK LORD ROTHSCHILD DUG UP EVIDENCE OF A LOST SOCIETY BURIED IN INFLATION.

THE JADED MAN; HIS PROTECTIVE SUIT IS MADE OF MANY "PHASES" JOINED BY THIN GOLD RESERVES BELIEVED TO BE A 'CONSERVATIVE' TO PREVENT THE DECAY OF THE CORPSE.

THE PRICELESS 'FLYING FARCE' FOUND ALONGSIDE THE BODY IS A SYMBOL OF **THE HEATH DYNASTY.**

September 30 Edward Heath. A Chinese Exhibition is mounted at the Royal Academy.

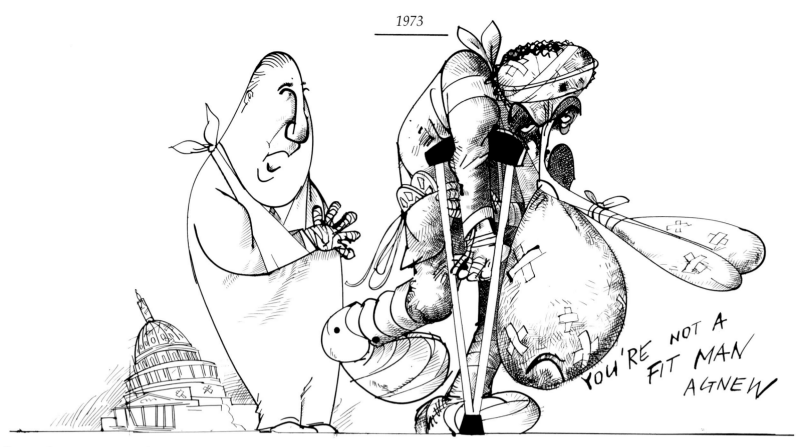

YOU'RE NOT A FIT MAN AGNEW

September 23 Vice President Spiro Agnew pleads guilty to tax fraud and resigns in order to avoid further prosecution.

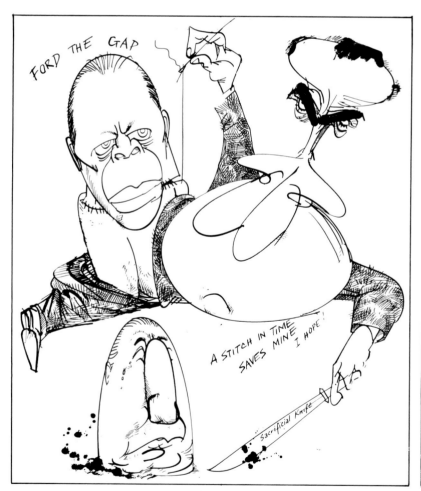

FORD THE GAP

A STITCH IN TIME SAVES MINE I HOPE!

Sacrificial Knife

October 14 After Agnew's resignation, Nixon takes on Gerald Ford as Vice President: the man that President Johnson said couldn't 'chew gum and walk at the same time'.

October 14 Soviet Party leader Leonid Brezhnev and Nixon. The United States begins airlifting arms to Israel in response to what is claimed to be a large-scale Soviet infusion of arms to Egypt and Syria.

STRIKING FOR OIL

November 25 Oil embargo. Golda Meir, President of Israel, at war with Egypt and Syria, is under pressure from oil sheiks. Sheikh Yamani, Saudi oil minister, is accused of using the oil squeeze as blackmail in hoping to swing Europe behind a pro-Arab Middle East settlement. President Sadat and King Faisal wish to draw the Middle East on their side, and persuade President Nixon to coax or drive the Israelis into what they would regard as an unfavourable settlement.

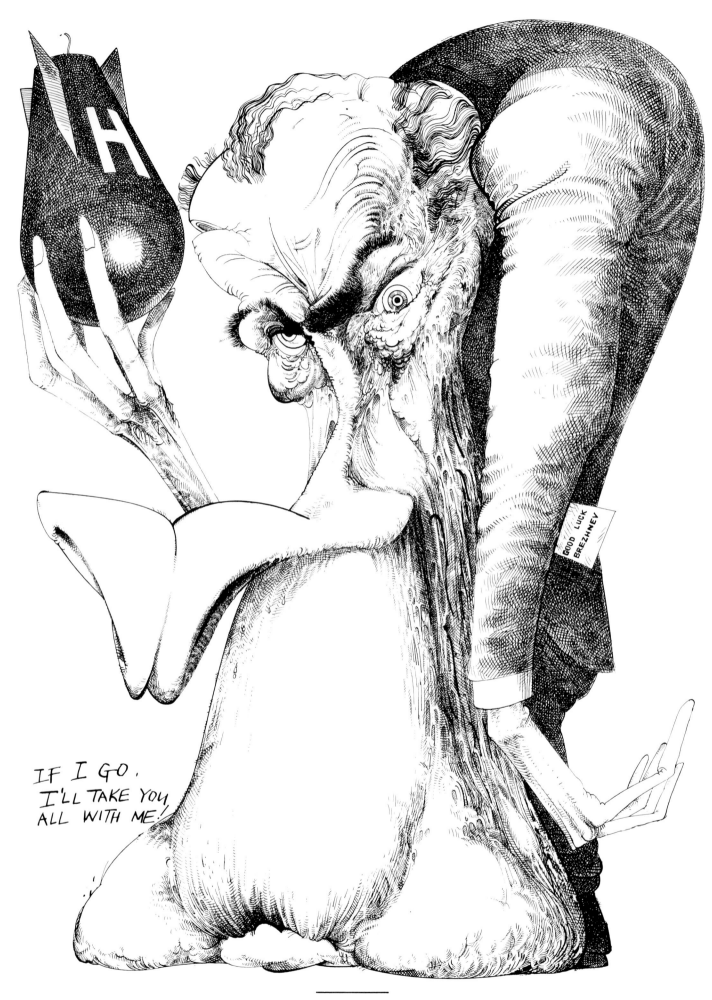

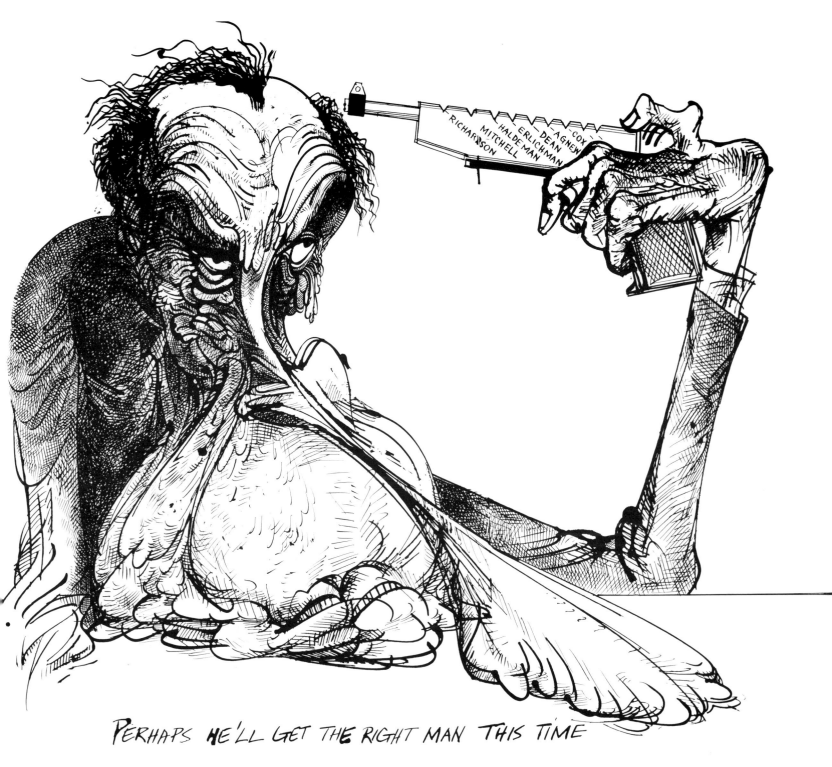

PERHAPS HE'LL GET THE RIGHT MAN THIS TIME

November 4 President Nixon blames and sacks everyone but himself. There is the sacking of Professor Cox, the resignation of Richardson; and the trials of Haldeman, Erlichman and Mitchell. The corruption attached to previous Presidencies is outdistanced.

◄ **October 28** Nixon refuses to go. At his delayed press conference the President tries to pass off Watergate as an irrelevance. He and Brezhnev, who visited America in June, are bringing peace to the world, he says. He then orders a nuclear alert over Russia and the Middle East and it is suggested he might be playing nuclear games to save his own skin. Impeachment becomes a serious possibility.

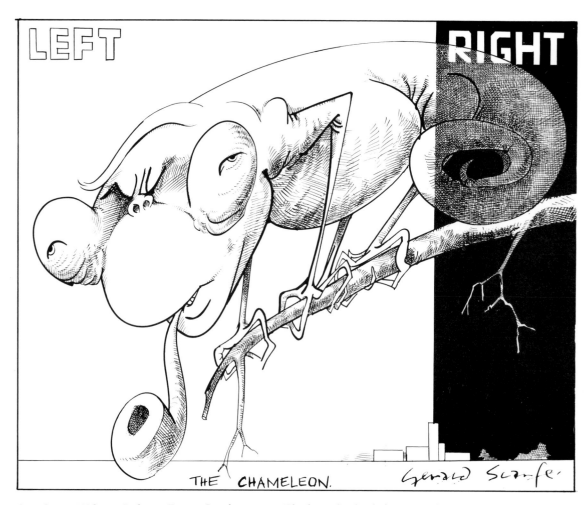

THE CHAMELEON.

October 7 Wilson. Labour Party Conference at Blackpool. The left wing of the Labour Party gains strength.

September 16 Heath and the proposed Channel Tunnel.

December 23 Christmas time, and Churchillian Heath soldiers on despite the coal strike and the power crisis bringing British industry to the brink of chaos. Heath has ordered a three-day working week, viewed with foreboding by industrialists who fear major economic damage to the country. The rail men, under Sidney Weighell, work to rule. In the miners' dispute the government suggests that the miners be paid for waiting time.

December 30 End of 1973 - nothing changes.

1974

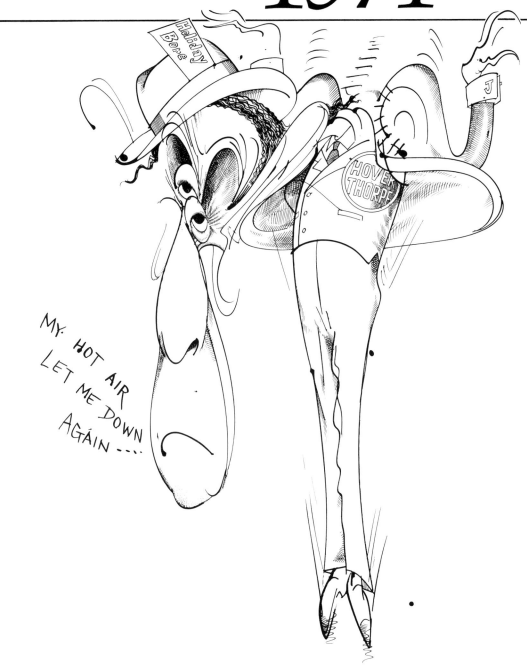

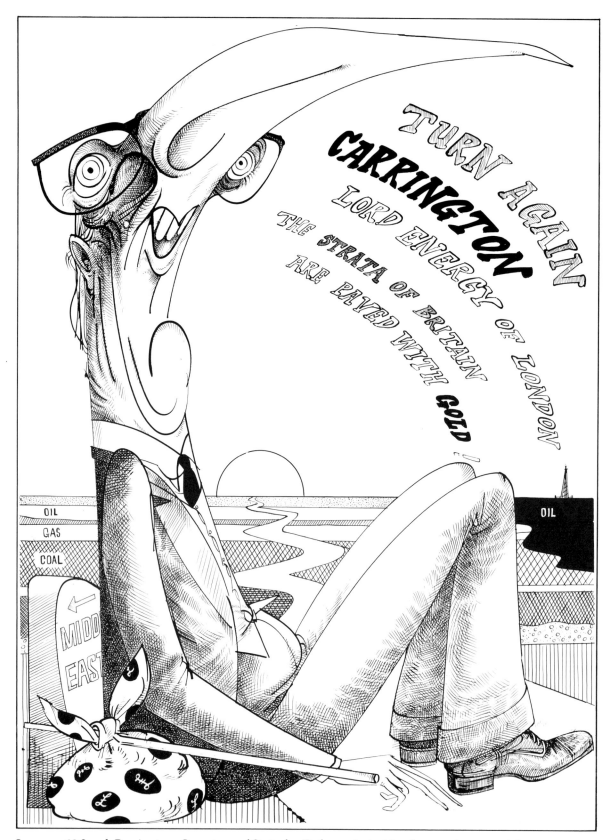

January 13 Lord Carrington, Secretary of State for Defence, is put in charge of reorganising Britain's energy industries and rescuing the country from national bankruptcy.

September 1 Jeremy Thorpe goes electioneering on a Hovercraft - which breaks down. He had been boring holiday-makers on beaches up and down the coastline.

I COULDN'T DO WORSE!

.... OR DID I?

Now. WHO RULES THE? COUNTRY ME—OR THIS RED HERRING

TWO CAN PLAY AT FRAUDULENT POLITICS MR·HEATH

I'M LEAVING

February 10 General Election. Edward Heath, his leadership collapsing, credibility gone, suffering the weakness of sterling, the energy crisis and the collapse of the electricity system and stunned by the long unbreakable miners' overtime ban, becomes obliged by a political necessity of his own making to hold a general election. He wishes to ask the country for its vote of confidence.

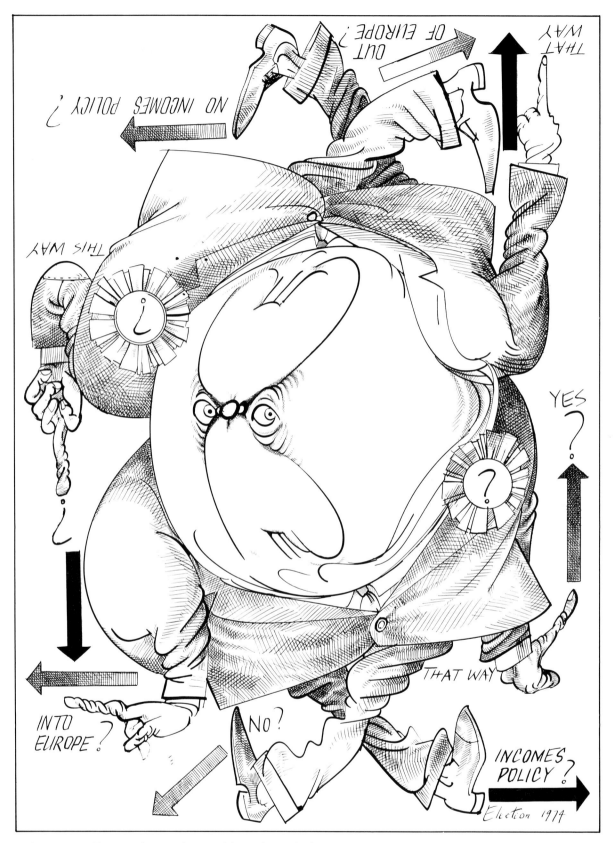

February 17 Election fever. The sparkling choice before the electorate: two-faced Wilson, Edward Heath, Jeremy Thorpe.

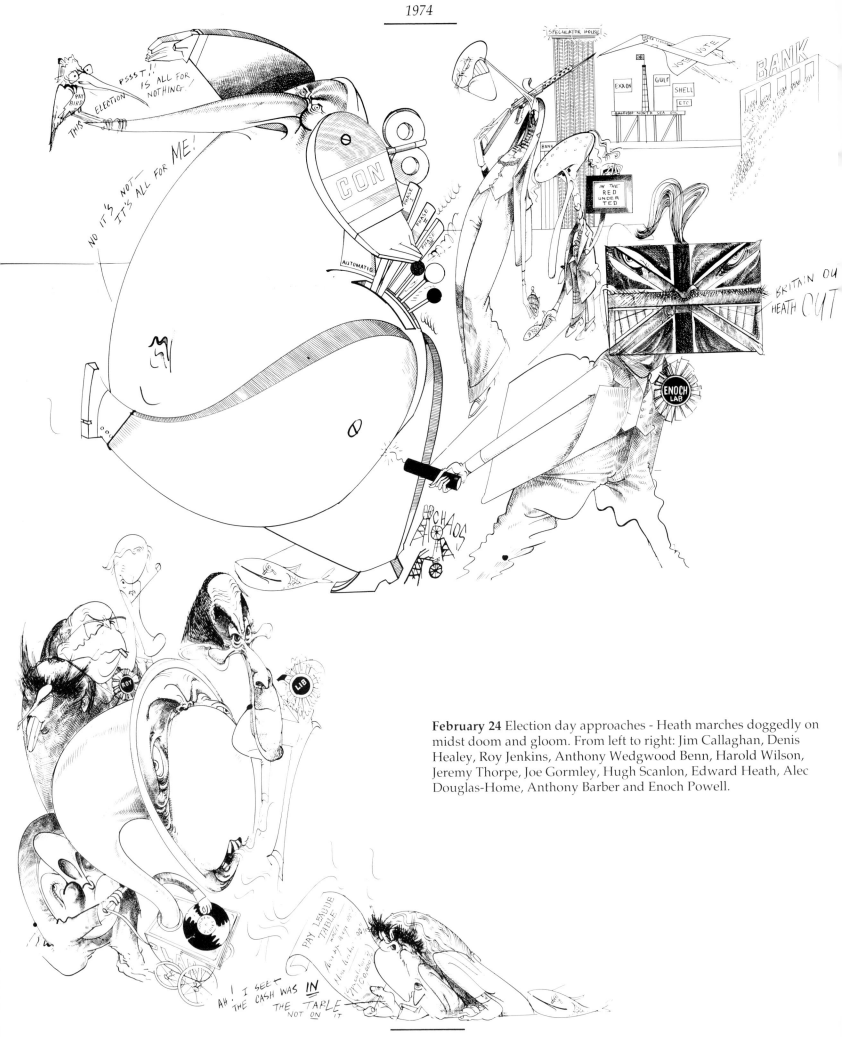

February 24 Election day approaches - Heath marches doggedly on midst doom and gloom. From left to right: Jim Callaghan, Denis Healey, Roy Jenkins, Anthony Wedgwood Benn, Harold Wilson, Jeremy Thorpe, Joe Gormley, Hugh Scanlon, Edward Heath, Alec Douglas-Home, Anthony Barber and Enoch Powell.

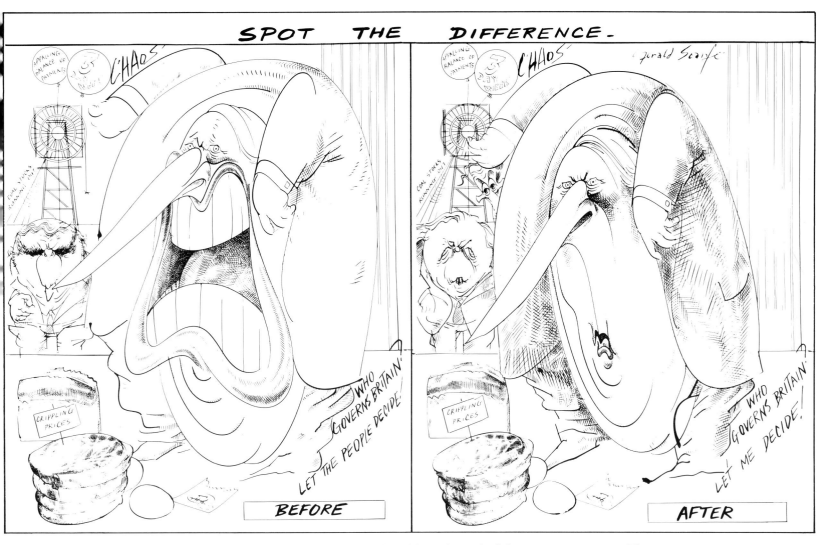

March 3 Heath loses the election. There is a massive Liberal vote, heralding the end of the two-party system. There is a stalemate between two parties without a coherent third party to hold the balance. Both big parties poll fewer-than-twice as many votes as the Liberals, but win more than 28 times as many seats. Tories have lost, but Labour has not won. A Tory-Liberal alliance is discussed. Thorpe looks around the House of Commons and says, 'One realises we are all minorities now - indeed some more than others', and he calls for a government of national unity to be formed. Heath hangs on for the 1st, 2nd and 3rd of March, but resigns on the 4th. Wilson forms a minority government.

April 7 Population explosion. In 1970 the world population is 4 billion, it is expected to double by the end of the century.
World Population Year.

THIS WEEK'S CASE FOR ADOPTION
SPECIAL OFFER—AS SEEN ON T.V.

April 28 Roy Mason, Minister of Defence, and Enoch Powell, Ulster Unionist.

◄

May 19 Enoch Powell, one of the cleverest minds in politics, is a thorn in the side of the Conservative Party, defying Mr Heath and being stridently anti-Market. He now delivers a conciliatory speech expressing his wish to return to Parliament. Adoption of children on TV is tried.

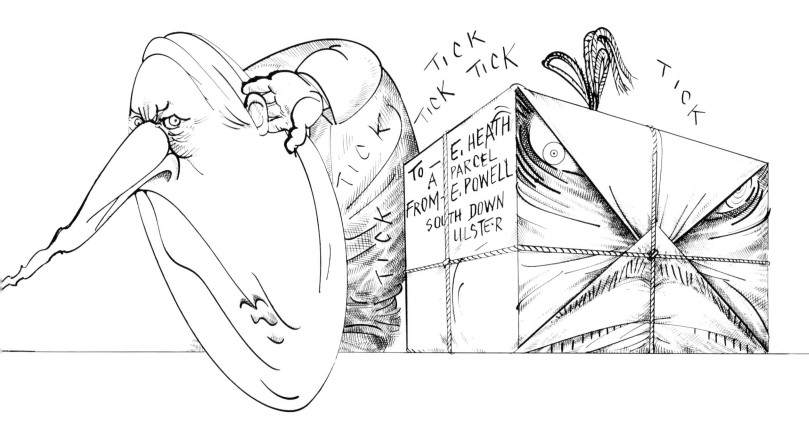

September 1 Enoch Powell, continually at war with Edward Heath. Powell hopes to return to Parliament by fighting for the Ulster parliamentary seat of South Down in the next general election. Parcel bombs are sent through the mail.

May 12 The Engineers' Strike. The AEUW seeks recognition as a non-union shop at Conmech by industrial action. The AEUW is taken to the Industrial Relations Court which finds in its favour but the AEUW shows its contempt for the Court by ignoring what it offered and consequently an award is made against them for the damage done to Conmech. They refuse to pay and the fine is paid by a group of businessmen - a secret gift. Michael Foot, Lord Goodman and Hugh Scanlon

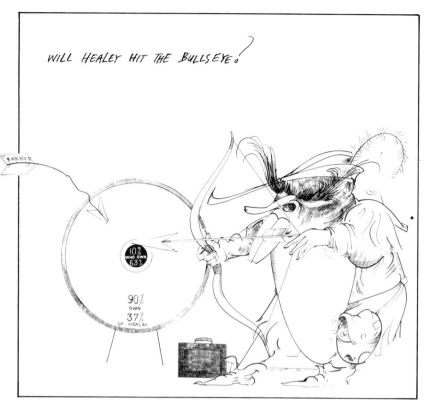

March 24 Denis Healey's first budget.

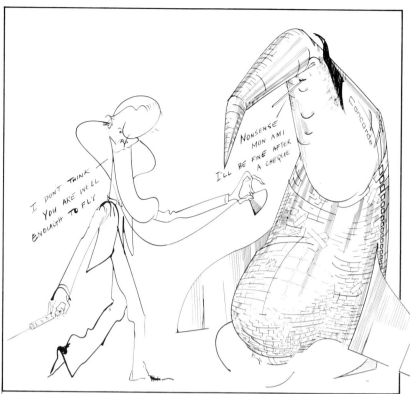

March 31 Anthony Wedgwood Benn, Minister of State for Industry, says that Concorde will be too expensive. President Georges Pompidou as Concorde.

June 2 Northern Ireland. Gerry Fitt, Craig, Faulkner, and Merlyn Rees, the Home Secretary.

July 7 Forced by NUPE, Barbara Castle (Minister of Health) ▶ clamps down on private medicine.

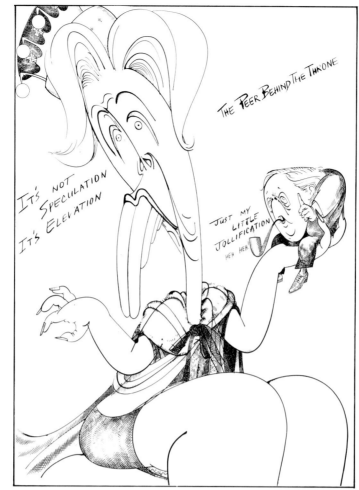

May 26 The brother of Lady Falkender (Harold Wilson's Private and very influential secretary) is accused of speculation.

July 28 Rogue Republican Elephant. The Elephants' Graveyard. The disgracing of the President. The Supreme Court rules that the President must surrender the tapes that he holds to the judiciary committee of the House of Representatives, in order that they can decide if he should be impeached. He surrenders the tapes but they are incomplete, parts having been deleted.

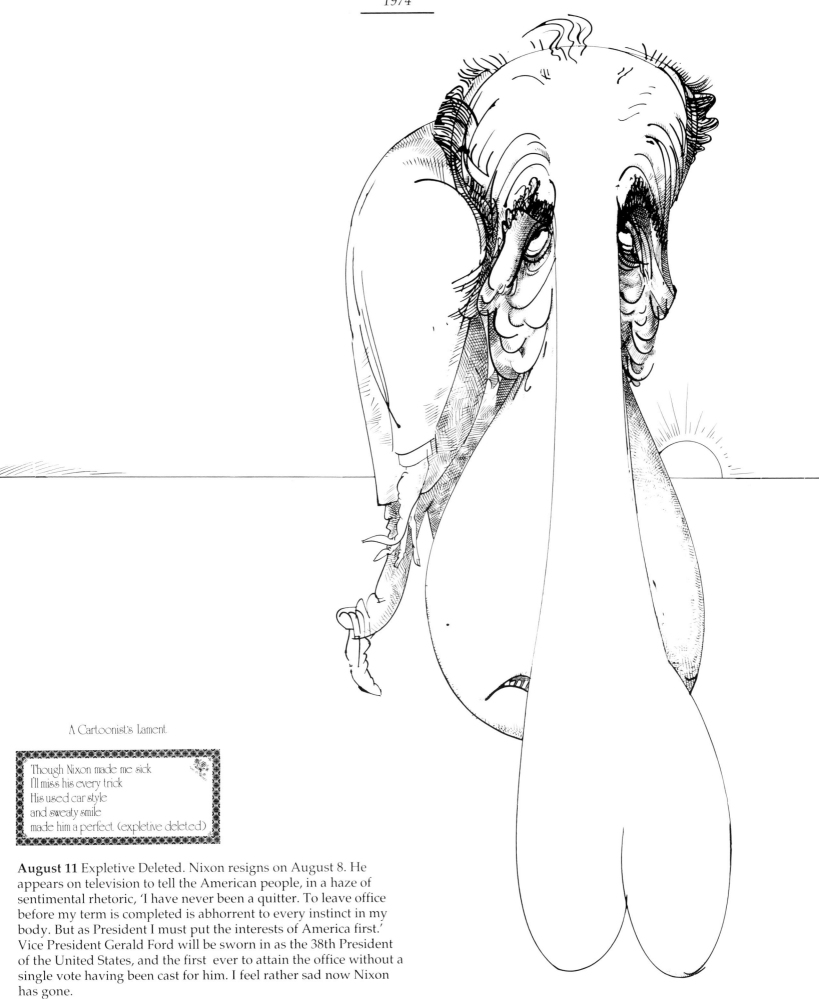

A Cartoonist's Lament

Though Nixon made me sick
I'll miss his every trick
His used car style
and sweaty smile
made him a perfect (expletive deleted)

August 11 Expletive Deleted. Nixon resigns on August 8. He appears on television to tell the American people, in a haze of sentimental rhetoric, 'I have never been a quitter. To leave office before my term is completed is abhorrent to every instinct in my body. But as President I must put the interests of America first.' Vice President Gerald Ford will be sworn in as the 38th President of the United States, and the first ever to attain the office without a single vote having been cast for him. I feel rather sad now Nixon has gone.

VICE PAYS OFF

September 15 Vice pays off: President Ford grants Nixon a full, free and absolute pardon, giving his reasons as Nixon's health and the fact that it would be impossible to receive a fair trial with the weight of public opinion against him. Some defend Ford by arguing that Nixon's particular abuses of power are rooted in American history, but others call it an error of judgement.

WILSON SEEKS ROYAL APPROVAL FOR ELECTION.

September 8 The TUC Brighton Congress. The Social Contract, Labour's election trump card, is a deal between government and unions in which unions undertake to moderate their wage claims in return for a package of economic and social reforms. Hugh Scanlon's 1,400,000 strong engineering union rejects it.

September 29 Harold Wilson has called a General Election to increase his majority. Harold Wilson plagued by the Scanlon Imp and the unworkable Social Contract. Thorpe says that the Liberals would be crazy to say no to a coalition if a chance were offered to carry through Liberal policies. Shirley Williams and Roy Jenkins, marketeers. Jeremy Thorpe. Inflation is the key issue. Wilson's group of Labour policies is failing. Mrs Thatcher's plans for subsidising mortgage interest rates and helping first-time house-buyers is a vote winner. Wage inflation is the dominant fear of the future, and an arrangement must be made with the unions. The Conservatives pour scorn on the Social Contract, although they had the similar Phases 1,2 and 3. Whitelaw and Heath. The most important discussion is the gathering threat to the economic system of half the world posed by the huge rises in Arab oil prices. The USA threatens to use its own power, in the form of grain, to make the Arabs more cooperative.

STRAYS TAKEN IN

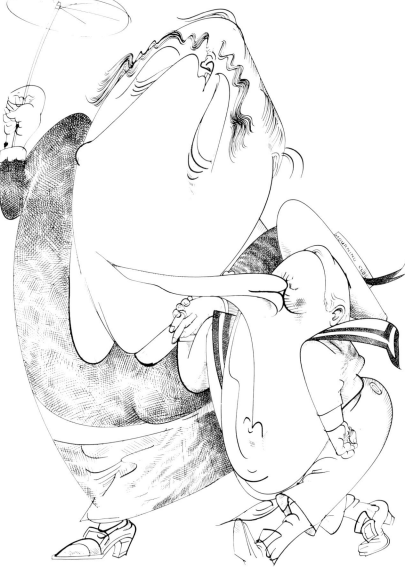

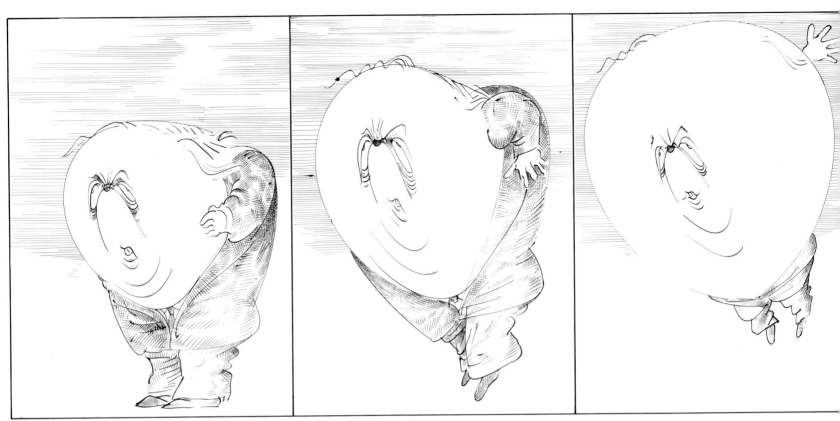

October 13 Prime Minister Wilson and Inflation. Economic crisis. There is talk of a Tory/Liberal coalition. Wilson wants to avoid the possibility of any alliance which would result in coalition. Wage-earners must accept a substantial lowering of their standard. Wilson wants the Liberals to do well to produce more Tory losses.

October 13 Edward Heath, Leader of the Opposition and Deflation. Heath's rigidity and misjudgement have taken Tories out of office. The 1922 Committee (composed of all Conservative back-bench MPs) meets to discuss who will be Heath's successor. Will it be Whitelaw, Joseph, Carr, Thatcher, du Cann?

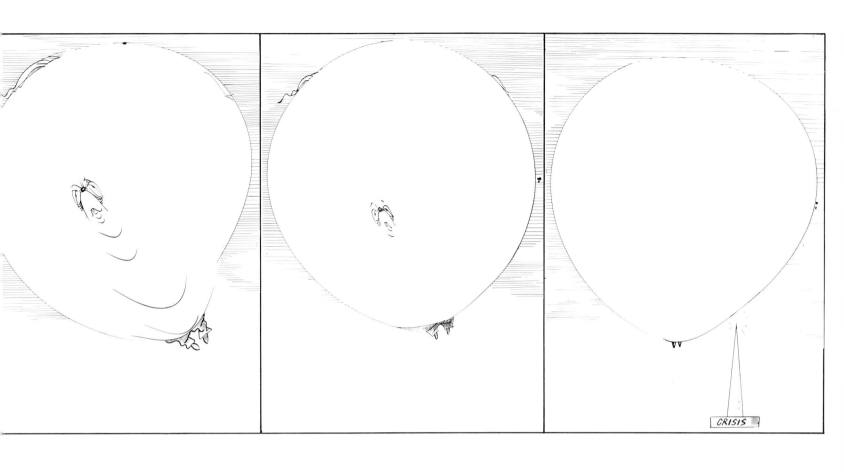

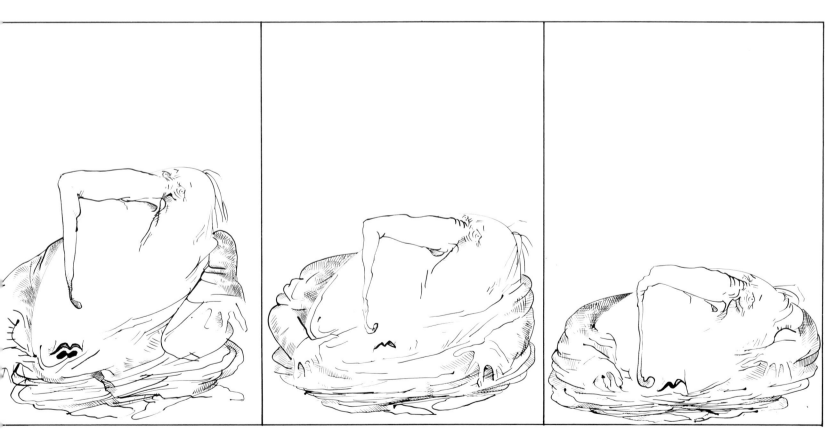

October 27 Enoch Powell - Thatcher on the blasted Heath - Whitelaw. The unpopular Heath is now disowned by his party. The larger part of the Conservative party wants a chance to choose a new leader. There is no obvious choice. Keith Joseph will have a powerful influence on future Tory thinking. He makes a speech about self-reliance and about the decline in individual and social morality.

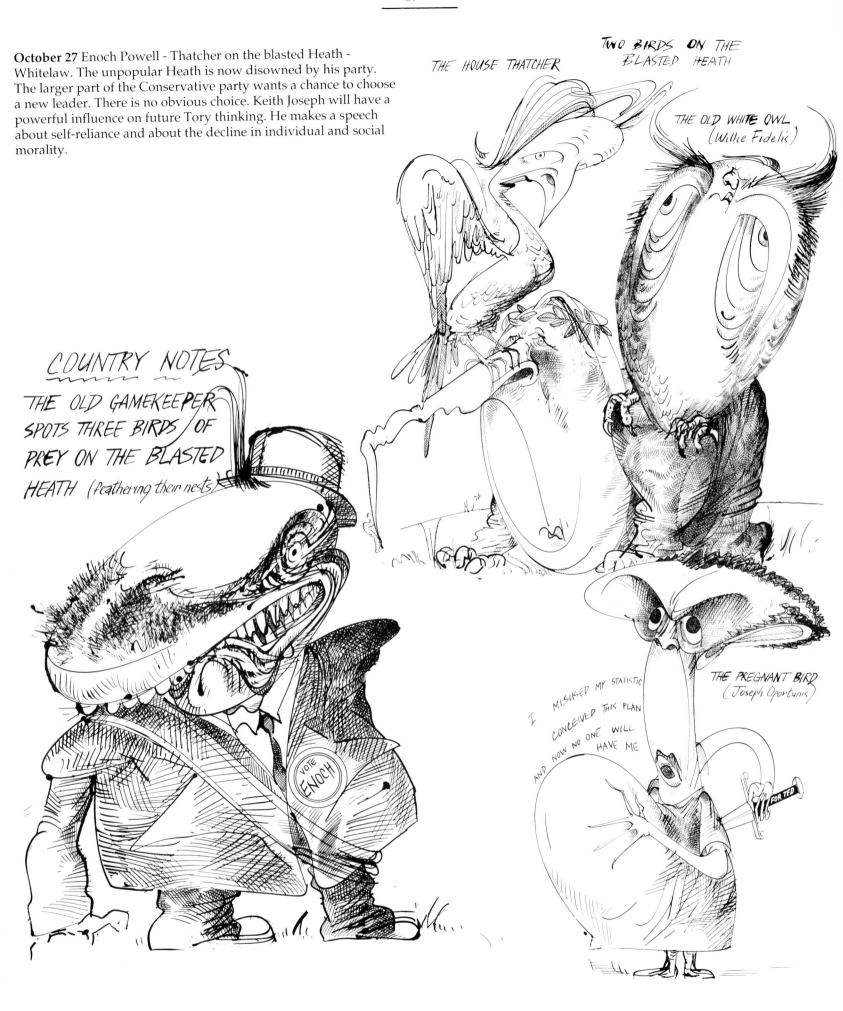

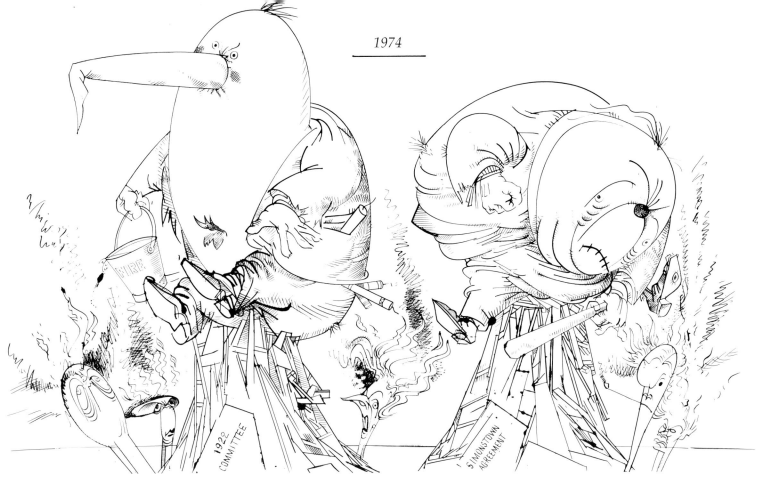

November 3 Guy Fawkes Night. Heath must go as Leader of the Tory Party. Is he ready to resign? Wilson in trouble over the Simonstown agreement (a naval cooperation with South Africa, while at the same time disavowing political involvement or approval of South Africa's policies).

November 10 Denis Healey, Chancellor of the Exchequer, approaches his budget on 12 November. His public spending cuts are thought to threaten British Rail's new era of high speed passenger transport and competitive freight services.

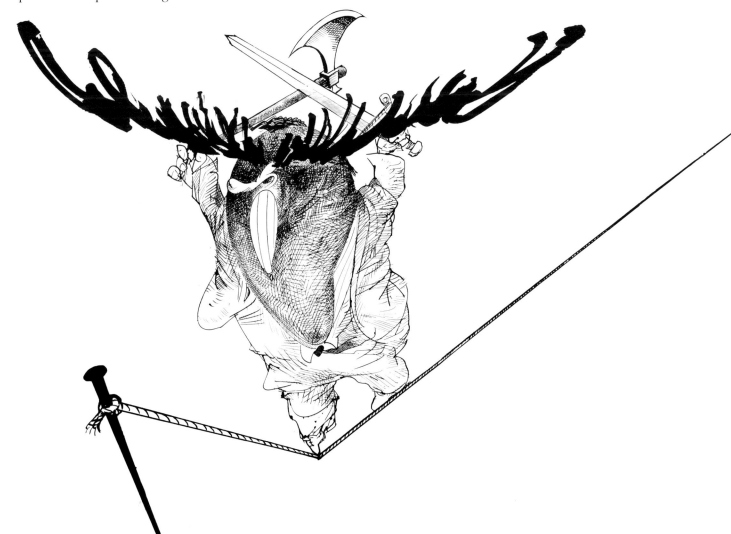

December 8 Talks are organised by South African Prime Minister John Vorster and three heads of African states to resolve the nine year dispute over black and white power sharing in Rhodesia. Ian Smith says No to the talks on the grounds that there is no promised cessation of terrorism

December 15 The boot is on the other foot: Ian Smith climbs down and agrees to free his black ▶ nationalist detainees and sit with them at a conference table and discuss majority rule.

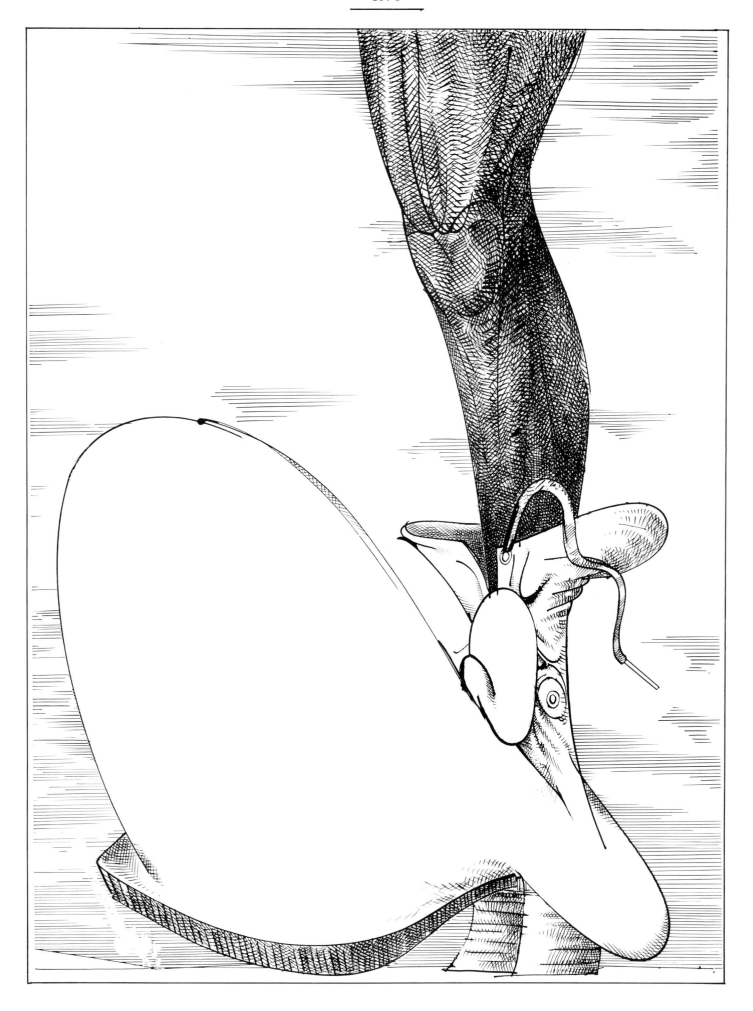

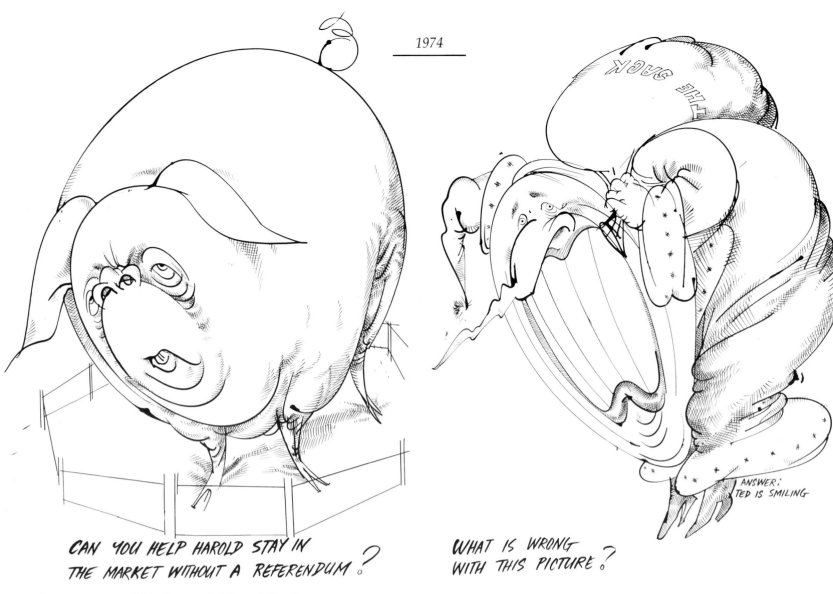

CAN YOU HELP HAROLD STAY IN THE MARKET WITHOUT A REFERENDUM?

WHAT IS WRONG WITH THIS PICTURE?

ANSWER: TED IS SMILING

December 24 Harold Wilson and Edward Heath

December 29 The Old Year - Wilson - goes out, and the New Year - Wilson - comes in, bringing with him the atmosphere of the 1930s.

1975

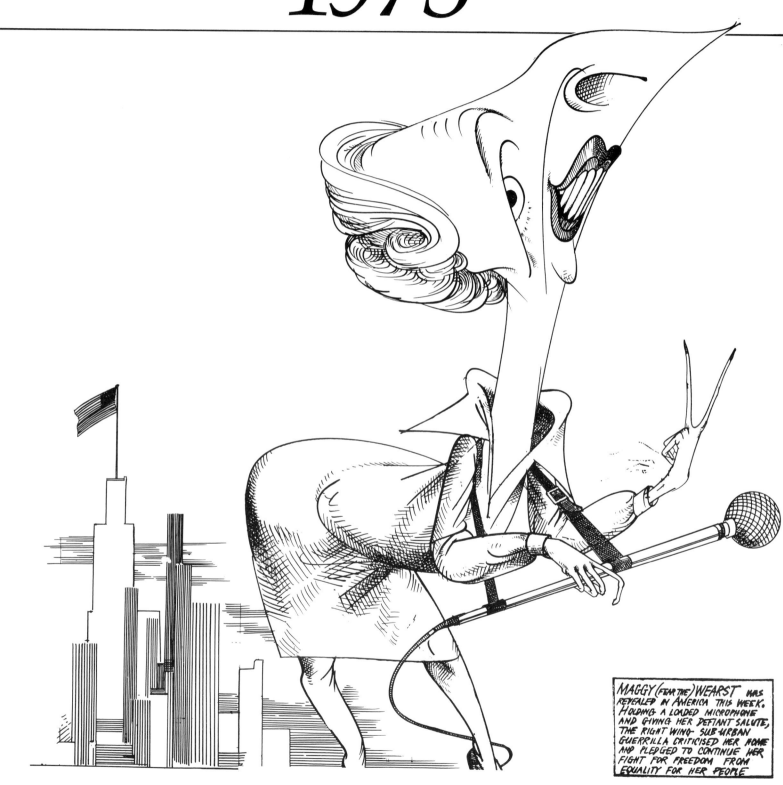

MAGGY (FEAR THE) WEARST was revealed in America this week. Holding a loaded microphone and giving her defiant salute, the right wing- sub-urban guerrilla criticised her home and pledged to continue her fight for freedom from equality for her people

◄ **September 21** Mrs Thatcher in America criticises Britain. Heiress Patty Hearst was kidnapped but apparently joined the guerillas of the Symbionese Front and was later seen raiding a bank.

January 5 Harold Wilson accuses unions of unrealistic demands while prices continue to rise.

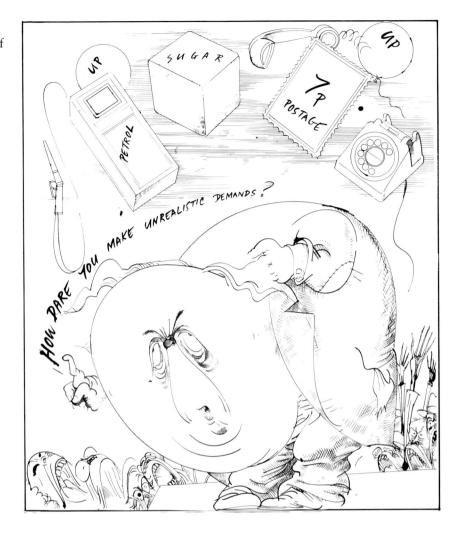

January 26 Harold Wilson as Groucho Marx, Peter Shore as his cigar, and the referendum as to whether to join Europe or not. Schmidt and d'Estaing look on.

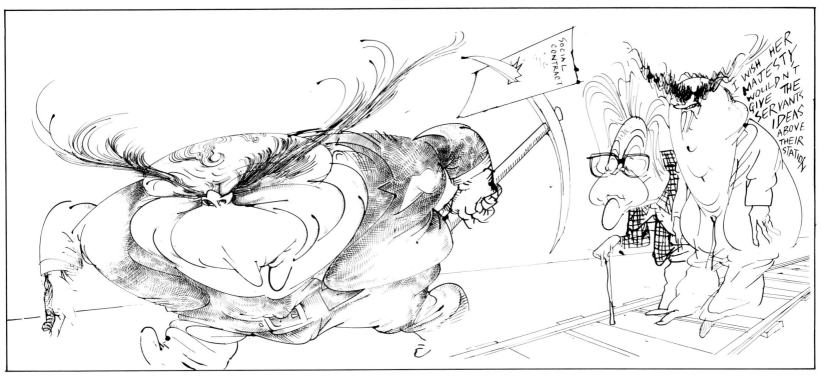

February 16 Joe Gormley, Michael Foot and Denis Healey. The Social Contract. Calls are heard to scrap and rewrite it.

February 9 All the dignity of pancake day. The Race for the Leadership of the Conservative Party. None of the five candidates has held any major offices of state. Willie Whitelaw (who it is thought will win the race), Margaret Thatcher (said to have a quick but suburban mind and at education was known as 'milk snatcher' and only partly effective, though she is already the prophet of the new monetarism), Francis Pym, Jim Prior, Geoffrey Howe, Alec Home and Heath.

February 23 Mrs Thatcher becomes the new leader of the Conservative party and picks her shadow cabinet. In come Maudling and Hailsham, out go Peter Walker, Robert Carr and Geoffrey Rippon.

March 2 Prime Minister Wilson calls a referendum to decide about Britain's entry into the Common Market. There are worries about parliamentary democracy, and Wilson is accused of holding the referendum in order to keep Labour together.

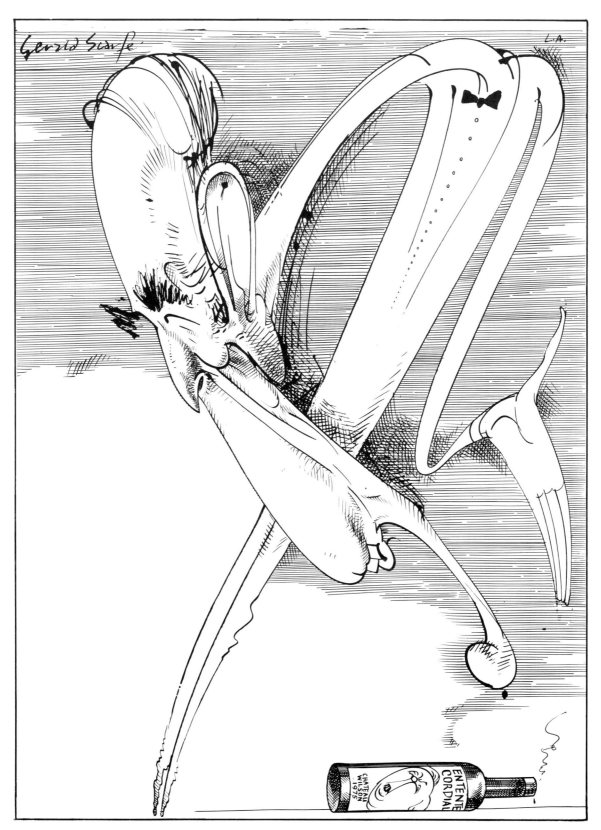

March 9 Giscard D'Estaing, Harold Wilson and Entente Cordiale

May 25 Into Europe: Evel Wilson. Evel Knievel was a dare-devil ▶ stunt man who jumped impossible obstacles on his motor bike.

June 1 The referendum on whether to join Europe.
NO: Michael Foot, Wedgwood Benn, Peter Shore, Jack Jones and Barbara Castle.
YES: James Callaghan, Harold Wilson, Reg Prentice, Margaret Thatcher, Denis Healey and Ted Heath.
Giscard d'Estaing of France and Schmidt of Germany look on. The vote is 'YES'.
▼

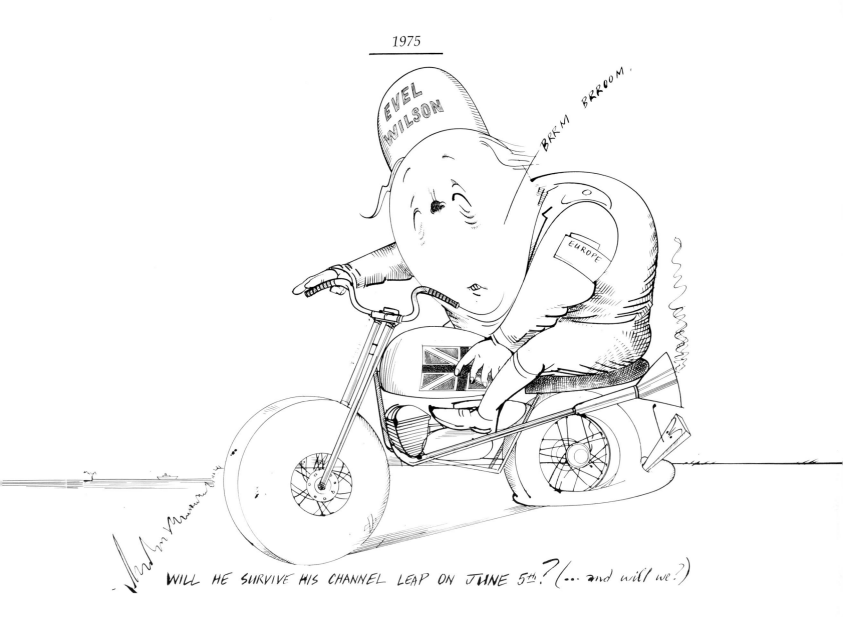

WILL HE SURVIVE HIS CHANNEL LEAP ON JUNE 5th? (... and will we?)

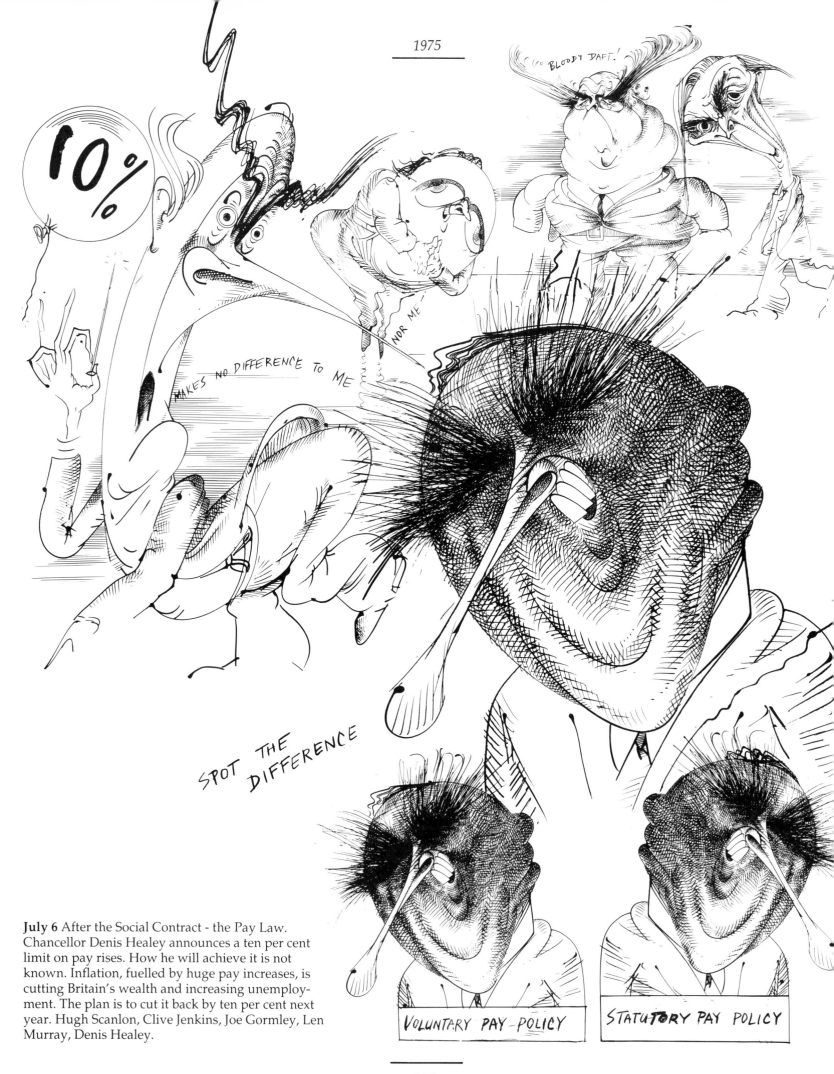

July 6 After the Social Contract - the Pay Law. Chancellor Denis Healey announces a ten per cent limit on pay rises. How he will achieve it is not known. Inflation, fuelled by huge pay increases, is cutting Britain's wealth and increasing unemployment. The plan is to cut it back by ten per cent next year. Hugh Scanlon, Clive Jenkins, Joe Gormley, Len Murray, Denis Healey.

August 3 The Gossip Columnist.

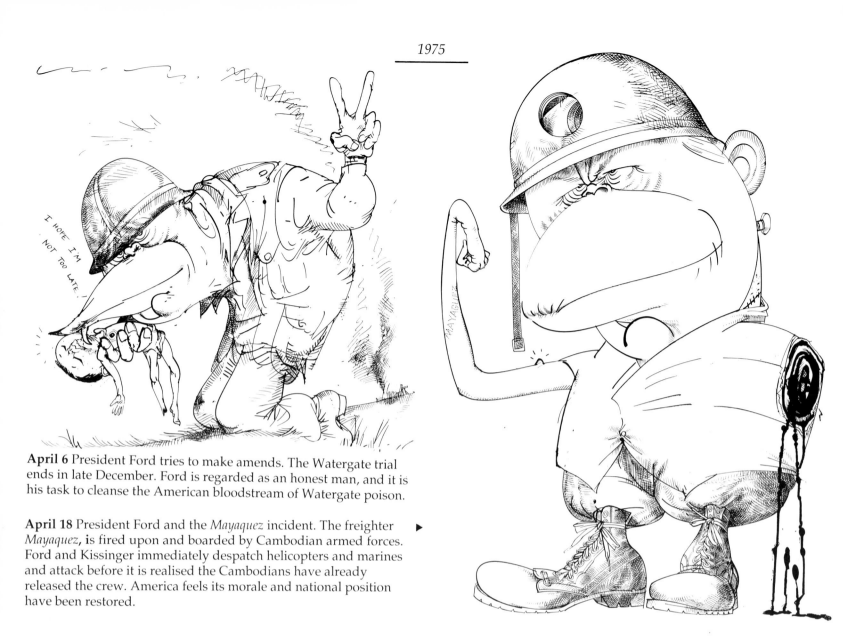

April 6 President Ford tries to make amends. The Watergate trial ends in late December. Ford is regarded as an honest man, and it is his task to cleanse the American bloodstream of Watergate poison.

April 18 President Ford and the *Mayaquez* incident. The freighter *Mayaquez*, **i**s fired upon and boarded by Cambodian armed forces. Ford and Kissinger immediately despatch helicopters and marines and attack before it is realised the Cambodians have already released the crew. America feels its morale and national position have been restored.

May 4 Now Ford finds himself in trouble over the everlasting problem of Vietnam. Presidents Washington, Taft, Lincoln, Kennedy, Johnson, Nixon, Ford, and trouble-shooter Kissinger.

Mount Rushmore 1975 — Gerald Scarfe

November 9 Ronald Reagan is ready to challenge for the Presidency. Gerald Ford is felt by
the public not to be truly in charge of foreign and defence policies. Because of his amateurism
and insecurity and in order to enforce his authority and gain respect he engineers and then
mishandles a cabinet shake-up. Nelson Rockefeller does not want to continue as Vice President.

October 26 General Franco of Spain dies.

September 7 The continual slaughter in pursuit of causes.

July 20 Considering the six pounds pay limit for all, Harold Wilson chooses a bad moment to give MPs a pay rise. Wilson's incomes policy is not substantially different in principle from the one he tried to destroy under the Conservative government

October 19 Barbara Castle, Minister of Health and Social Security, and the malaise in the National Health Service. There is a dispute over junior hospital doctors' pay. Mrs Castle contemplates the abolition of pay beds in hospitals and of Private Practice itself.

December 7 Hospitals closed by strikes.

October 12 Mrs Thatcher, at her first conference as leader of the party, in Blackpool. In January
next year the Soviet newspaper *Red Star* names her the Iron Lady.

1976

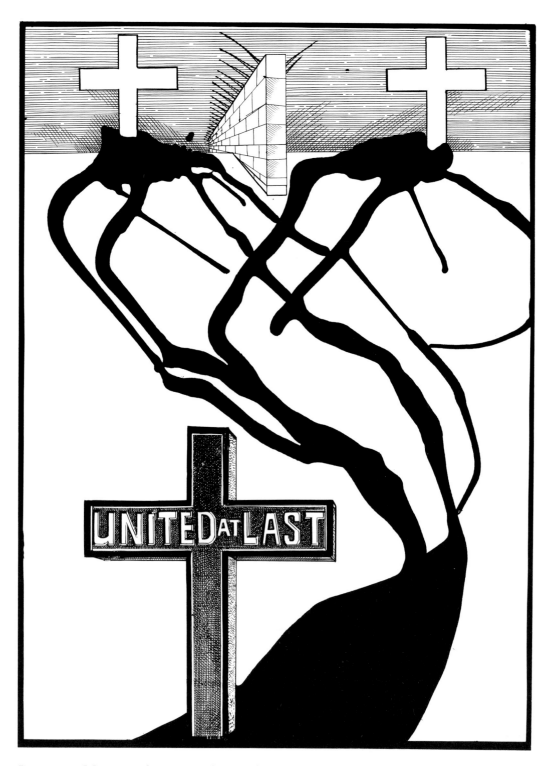

January 11 More murders in Northern Ireland. The White Cross massacre. Ten Protestants are killed by the South Armagh unit of the Provisional IRA. 150 SAS men fly to Northern Ireland under cover of darkness.

◄ **September 19** David Steel, made leader of the Liberal Party in July, hopes for a coalition.

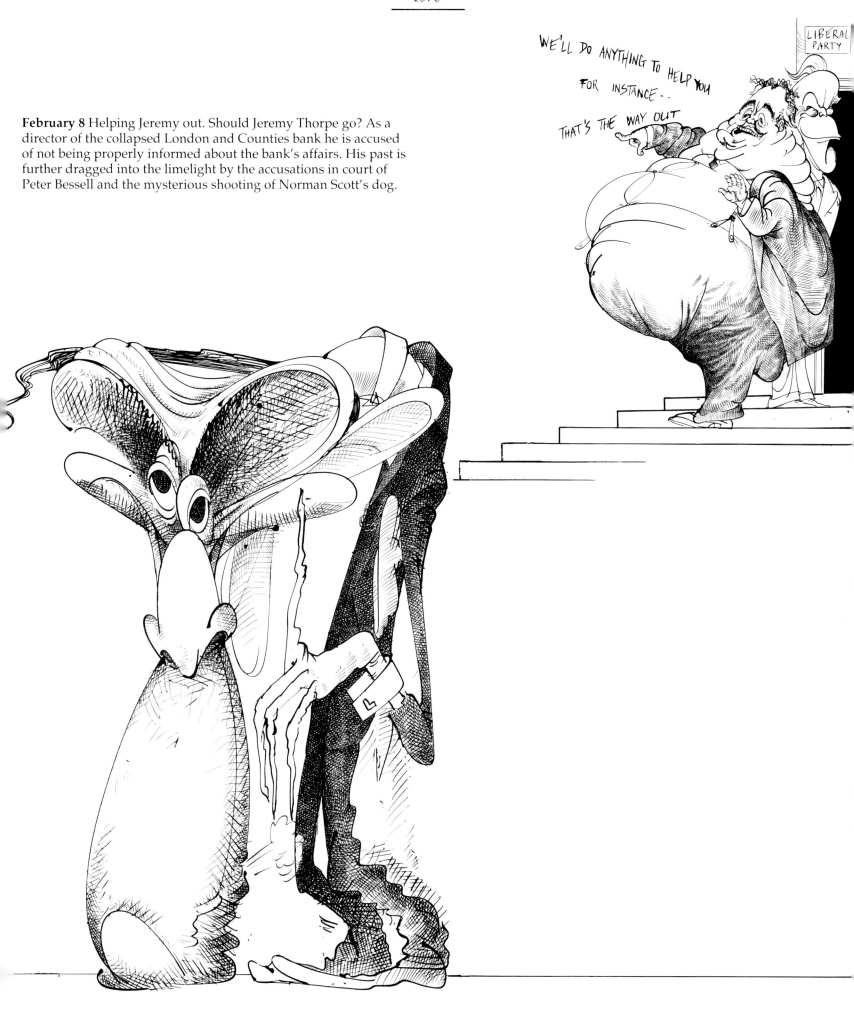

February 8 Helping Jeremy out. Should Jeremy Thorpe go? As a director of the collapsed London and Counties bank he is accused of not being properly informed about the bank's affairs. His past is further dragged into the limelight by the accusations in court of Peter Bessell and the mysterious shooting of Norman Scott's dog.

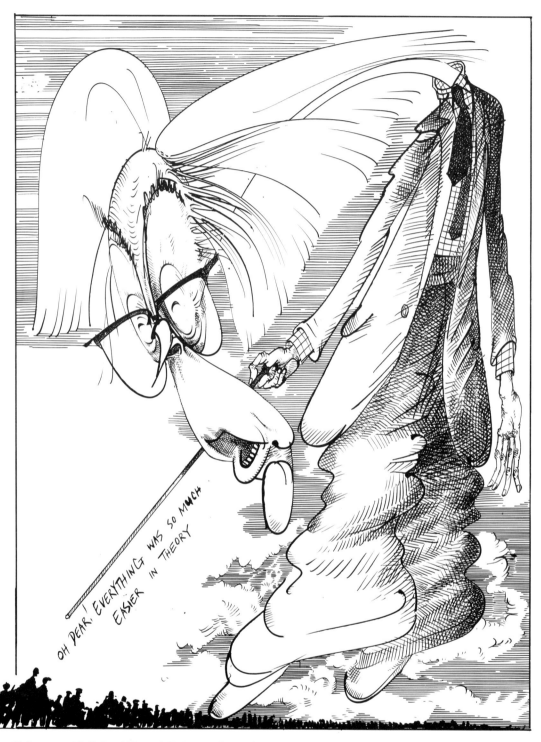

February 1 Michael Foot, Minister of Employment, finds theory easier than practice. He is replaced in April.

March 21 Labour Pains: the struggle for the leadership of the Labour party. Foot is ahead but Callaghan is the more popular. Foot talks about the unshakeable alliance between the Labour Government and the Trade Union movement. Benn, Foot, Callaghan, Jenkins, Crosland and Healey.

March 28 Spring. The contenders for leader of the Labour party: the field narrows. Mr Foot has the party's affection, but it is thought he would lose an election. Mr Healey's rugged intellect is admired, but Callaghan is thought to be the most capable.

February 22 Smith's Last Stand. Ian Smith continues to ignore the tidal wave of black resentment but a Cuban and Soviet intervention in Angola threatens a possible invasion over the Mozambique border. Will Smith come to terms with the Nationalists in Rhodesia and move towards one man one vote?

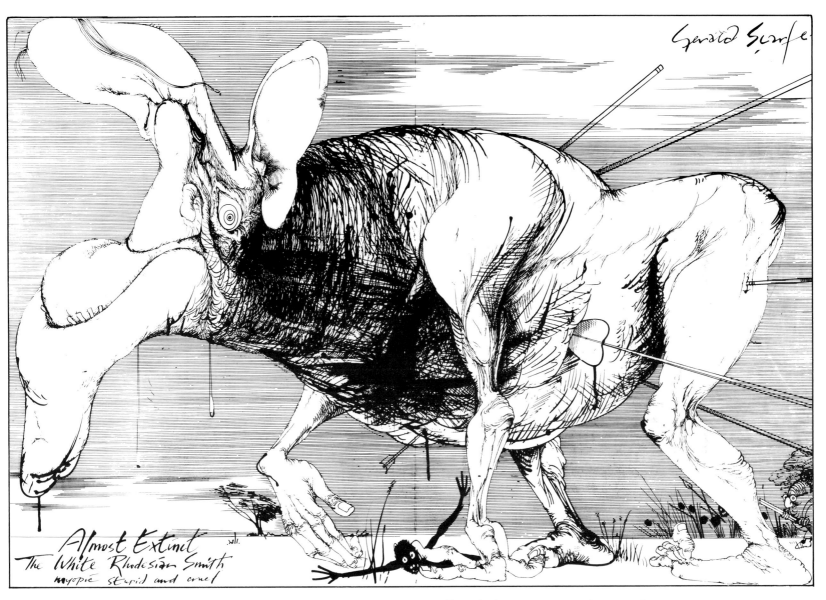

Almost Extinct
The White Rhodesian Smith
Myopic stupid and cruel

May 2 The Smithites are forced to face facts. Dr Kissinger, the showbiz travelling diplomat, in a speech in Lusaka, encourages black Africans to oppose Smith's white minority regime in Rhodesia. Ian Smith, humiliated by the Cuban and Soviet intervention in Angola, sees the end approaching.

September 26 Dr Kissinger hands Ian Smith a document saying, Rhodesia agrees to black majority rule in two years. 'You want me to sign my own suicide note,' says Smith.

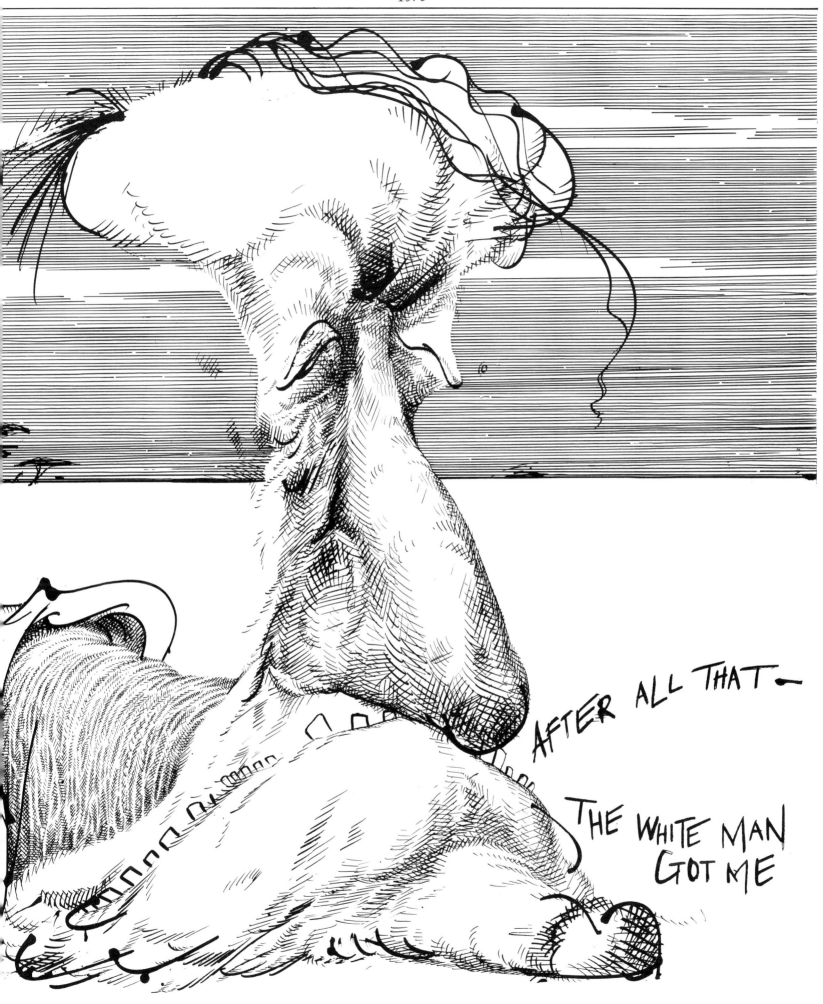

AFTER ALL THAT—

THE WHITE MAN GOT ME

April 18 Denis Healey
Humpty Healey sits on a wall
Will Humpty Healey have a great fall?
Or will Murray's forces and Jack Jones's men
Bring Healey and unions together again?

April 25 Harold Wilson accepts his knighthood.

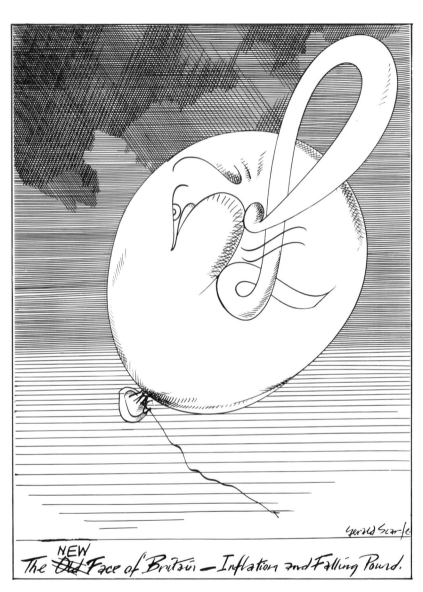

The NEW ~~Old~~ Face of Britain — Inflation and Falling Pound.

April 4 Callaghan is made Prime Minister on April 5. His first task will be the fortunes of the pound.

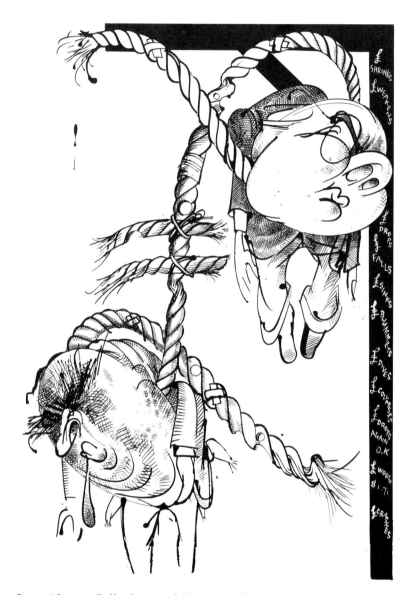

June 6 James Callaghan and Denis Healey. The pound falls.

May 16 The Ashes rising from the Phoenix: Jeremy Thorpe resigns as leader of the Liberal Party and Jo Grimond, party leader from 1956-67, takes over in the interim. David Steel is elected on July 11.

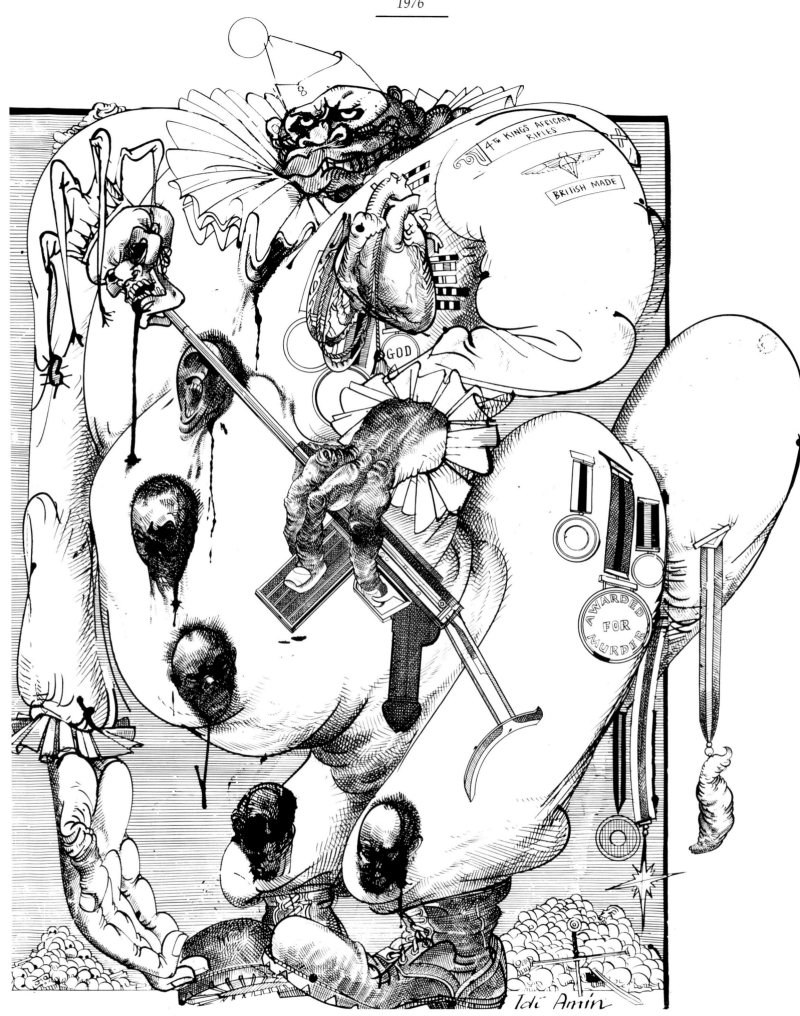

4TH KINGS AFRICAN RIFLES

BRITISH MADE

GOD

AWARDED FOR MURDER

Idi Amin

July 25 Black Power demonstrations at the Montreal Olympics.

◄ **June 13** Idi Amin.

May 23 Gerald Ford continues his run for re-election as President.

July 18 The arrival of Jimmy Carter, Democratic candidate in the ▶ Presidential race and peanut farmer from Plains, Georgia. People are puzzled and unsure about his policies, character, judgement and his much-advertised Christian belief. Walter Mondale is his running mate.

THE SAVIOUR ARRIVES

MAINTAINING CIVILISATION

August 15 Oppression continues in South Africa.

RON and JERRY
AND THE GEORGIA CAT

August 22 While Presidential hopefuls Ronald Reagan and Ford slug it out, Jimmy Carter gains ground with amazing rapidity. Ford has done his limited best with a difficult period of American politics. Reagan waves the flag, calls for more guns, ships, and appeals to the nationalistic and the chauvinistic.

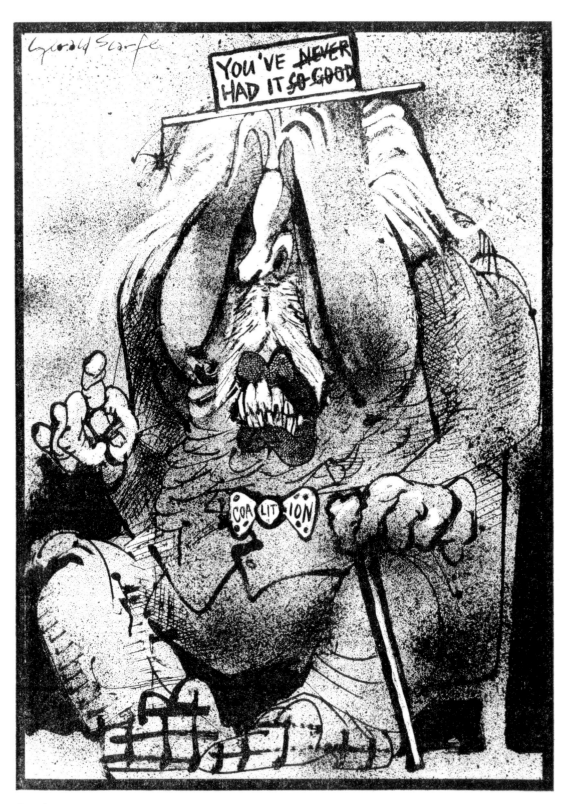

October 24 Ex-Prime Minister Harold MacMillan pronounces on the state of the country. 'You've never had it so good' was one of MacMillan's political quotes.

October 3 Blackpool Labour party Conference. Economic crisis. The squeeze. And the pound falls dramatically. Must support the pound and cut public spending. Factories are half-idle. Callaghan and Healey borrow money from the International Monetary Fund. The IMF was set up to enable countries to ride out storms without undue damage to themselves and world trade. Britain is granted a £5 billion standby credit by our partners. Desperate times.

October 10 Denis Healey takes an injection from the IMF. Margaret Thatcher at the Brighton Tory Conference.

November 14 Prime Minister James Callaghan - Labour is split left
and right as usual. The Conservatives are gaining in popularity
and have won several by-elections.

PETER PAN FINDS AN OLD SHADOW

THROWING THE THATCHER

November 21 Margaret Thatcher selects her new shadow cabinet, showing a move to the right. John Davies replaces the apathetic Reginald Maudling. Also in the cabinet: John Biffen, Tom King, Teddy Taylor and Dr. Rhodes Boyson.

December 12 Heath and Thatcher disagree about devolution in Scotland. Heath criticizes the bill which has certain faults with regard to finance where responsibility was divorced from power.

December 19 Denis Healey's Christmas budget is a package of public spending cuts and tax increases. A last chance for the country to recover its well-being and to get the economy right.

1977

HAPPY NEW YEAR
(WELL YOU NEVER KNOW...)

This is the first recorded cheerful work by Gerald Scarfe and, he said yesterday, probably the last.
Meanwhile, The Sunday Times, too, wishes its readers a happy new year

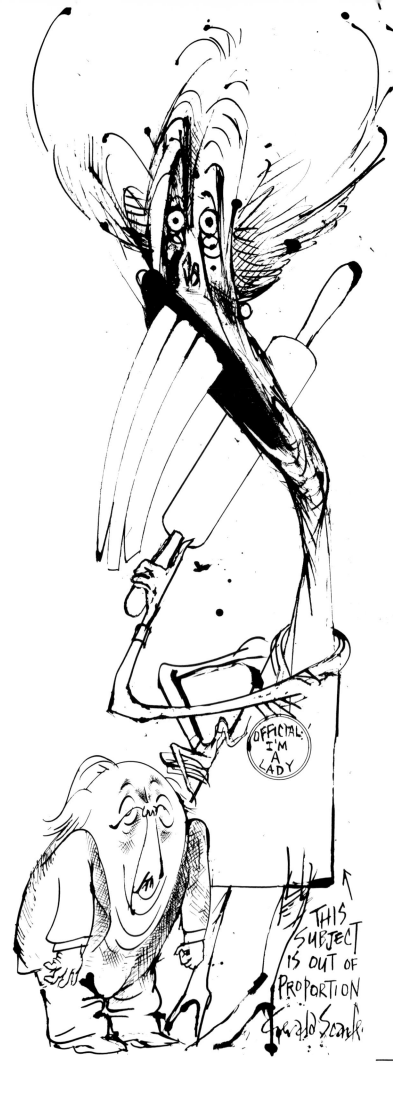

THIS SUBJECT IS OUT OF PROPORTION

OFFICIAL: I'M A LADY

 January 2 Optimistic cartoon.

February 13 Marcia Falkender. The personal and political secretary of the Prime Minister wielded great influence from 1964 to 1970. She was the architect of the 1970 June election (which Labour lost). Wilson causes an honours scandal by giving her a peerage.

March 27 The Pact: times are bad for Callaghan. The government has barely survived a vote of confidence. Can they hold off an election until North Sea oil flows in? The government's chance of achieving an effective pay restraint looks extremely poor. There is much social and industrial rebellion and the inflation rate has reached 16.6%. An agreement is reached between the government and the TUC to operate a pay restraint. Labour plus Liberals adds up to a majority and shores up the rocky government. Callaghan says Yes to a pact with David Steel.

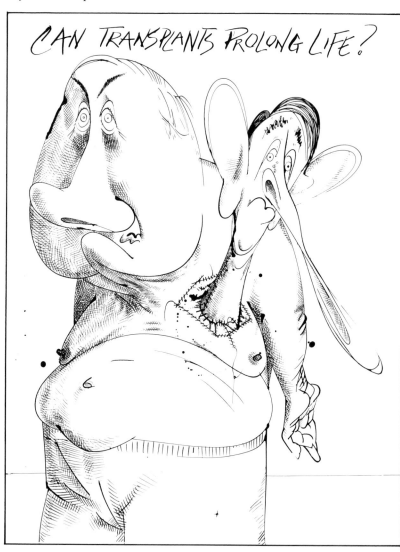

CAN TRANSPLANTS PROLONG LIFE?

February 27 Michael Foot - Devolution. Dividing the United Kingdom into financially separate parts, decentralising government. The Devolution Bill is among the worst-conceived and-executed constitutional measures ever introduced by government. It has no clarity about where ultimate legal and financial responsibility lies and no control over the spread of bureaucracy. The Commons effectively kill the bill by refusing to truncate a decision on it and denying it a guillotine.

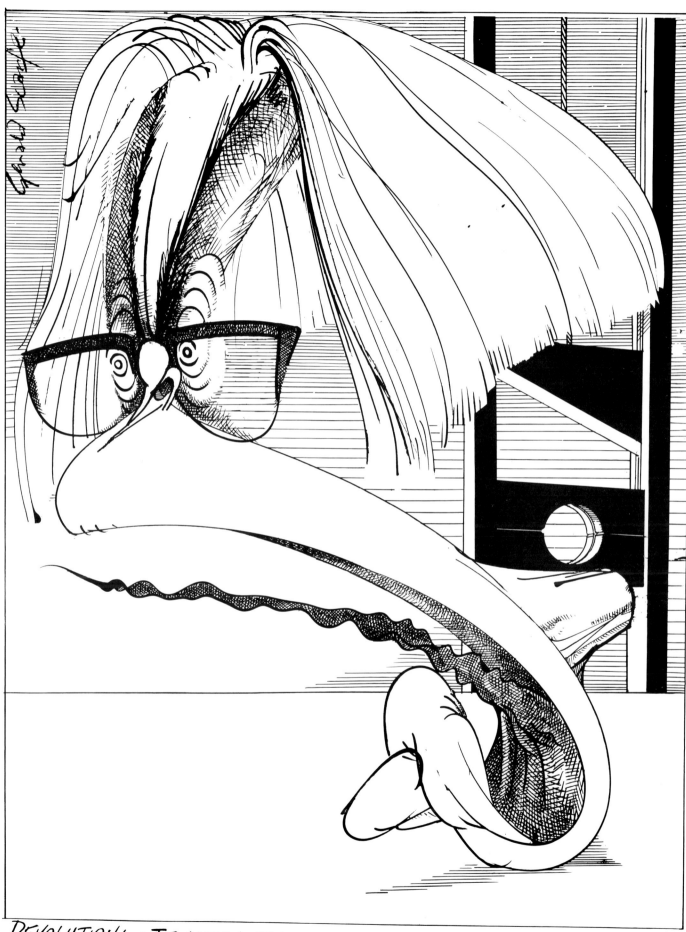

DEVOLUTION:— THE CAUSING OF ANYTHING TO DESCEND OR FALL UPON;— OXFORD ENGLISH DICTIONARY

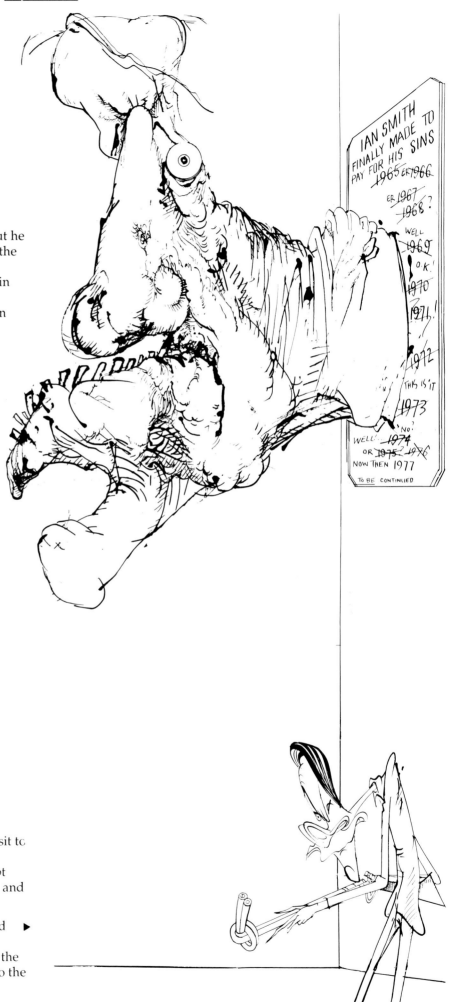

February 20 Idi Amin is still viewed by the world as a clown but he continues his murdering way. The arrest and sudden death of the Ugandan Archbishop Luwum and two ministers bring cries of atrocity and gross violation of human rights. It is said that Amin keeps severed heads in his fridge. Amin plans to attend the Queen's Jubilee celebrations and Prime Ministers' Conference in London in June. There are strong hints he should stay away. He does.

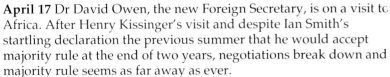

April 17 Dr David Owen, the new Foreign Secretary, is on a visit to Africa. After Henry Kissinger's visit and despite Ian Smith's startling declaration the previous summer that he would accept majority rule at the end of two years, negotiations break down and majority rule seems as far away as ever.

September 4 The Anglo-American plan for Rhodesia. Dr David ▶ Owen, the Foreign Secretary, causes alarm in Rhodesia, by announcing that the present guerilla forces will form the basis of the new Zimbabwe army to be used during the transition period to the new consitution.

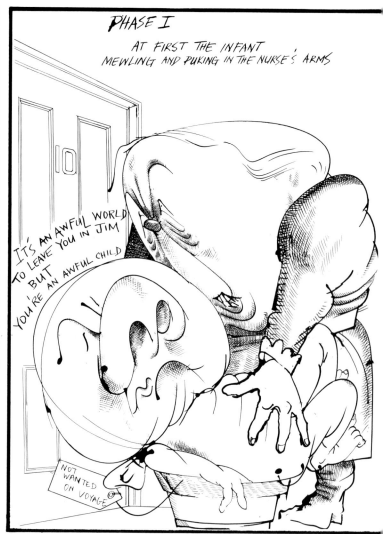

April 10 Margaret Thatcher hopes for an election in the autumn.
After the appalling record of decline, failure and stagnant gloom,
the depth of the Labour government's unpopularity is reflected in
their loss at the Stetchford by-election. Princess Anne is expecting a baby.

July 17 The Story of Jim Callaghan in Three Phases. Callaghan
takes over when Wilson goes - government joins the Lib-Lab pact
to survive. There have been two annual agreements between the
government and the TUC and the third phase is under difficulties

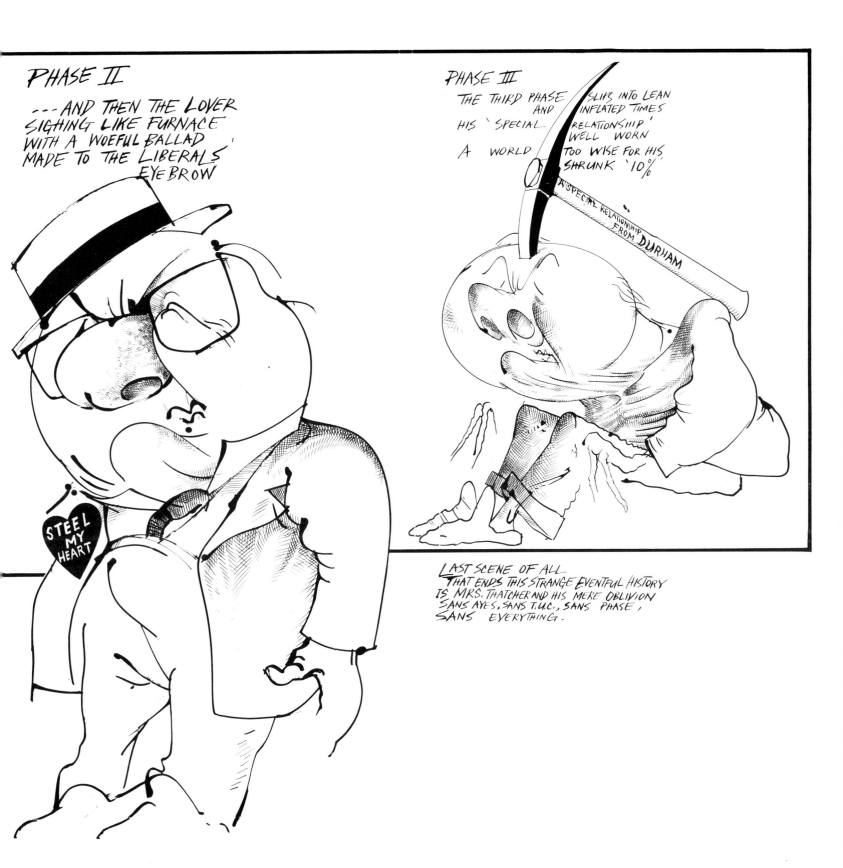

LAST SCENE OF ALL
THAT ENDS THIS STRANGE EVENTFUL HISTORY
IS MRS. THATCHER AND HIS MERE OBLIVION
SANS AYES, SANS T.U.C., SANS PHASE,
SANS EVERYTHING.

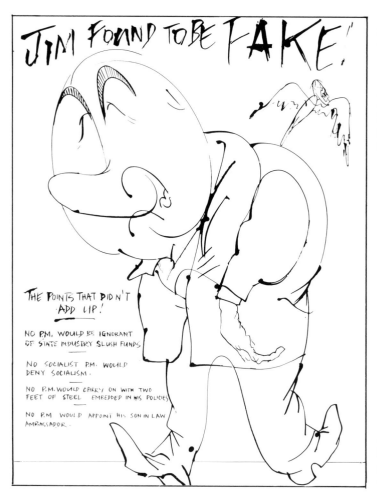

May 15 Prime Minister Jim Callaghan promotes his son-in-law Peter Jay to be British Ambassador in Washington.

May 22 James Callaghan. The slush fund affair. The Daily Mail reveals that Leyland operated a slush fund paying bribes for foreign contracts. It is followed by a revelation that a document in the case is forged.

April 24 Jimmy Carter, elected as the 39th President of the United States in February, campaigns to save energy. Carter has plans to stop the enormous waste, and to make America less vulnerable to the dictates of Saudi Arabia and Iran.

August 28 Callaghan and Steel enter Phase 3. There are strikes at Heathrow and unemployment rises.

November 13 Merlyn Rees, the Home Secretary, considers what to do about the firemen's strike.

August 14 Denis Healey's Budget.

South African newspaper - - - -
White only

- - - - - this way they don't get any bad news.

October 23 South African newspapers are censored. Under Mr Vorster's ruling Nationalist party the Minister of Justice has ditched freedom of the press. Steve Biko's black consciousness movement, clearly acting within the limits laid down by the law, is banned. (Biko is arrested and dies in jail.)

November 27 Ian Smith. One man one vote is achieved in Rhodesia with little protest from the ▶ whites. Despite Smith's rallying cry of 'No Majority Rule in my Lifetime', the guerilla war, sanctions and 12 years of isolation have taken their toll.

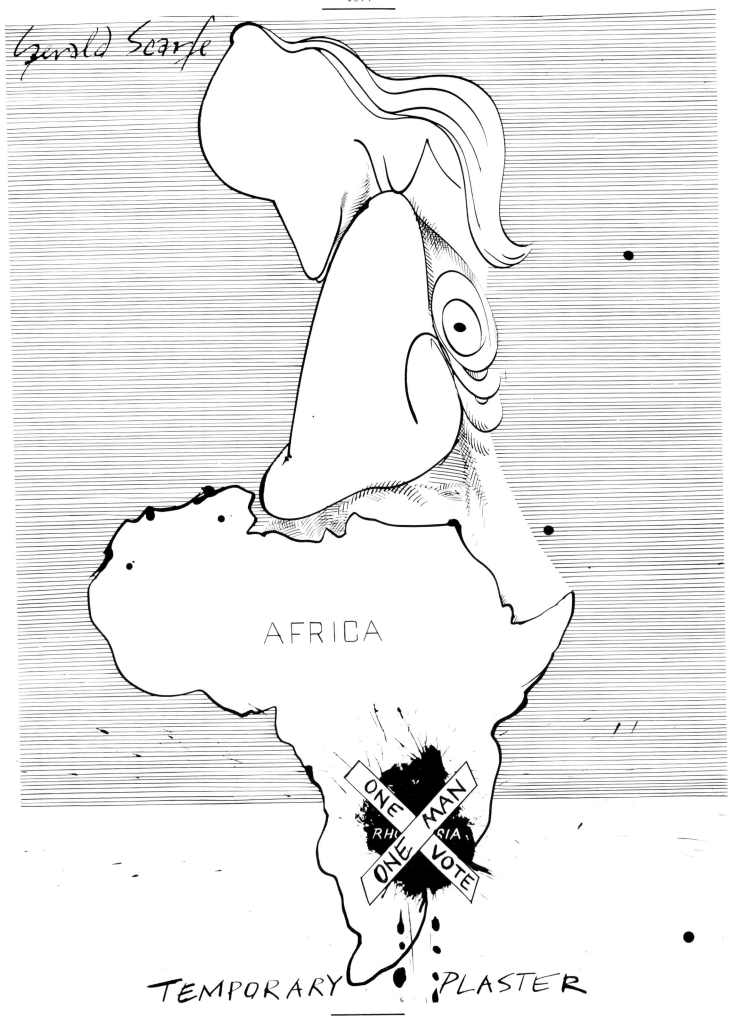

December 18 Callaghan and the pact with Steel. Steel wants proportional representation.

1978

STILL. UNDESTROYED BY MRS. THATCHER

January 15 Callaghan as the Graham Sutherland portrait of Churchill, thought to have been destroyed by Lady Churchill.

◄ **July 23** Jim Callaghan. Denis Healey's new pay policy. 5% limit on wages. Callaghan's chances of winning an election are worse than Mrs Thatcher's.

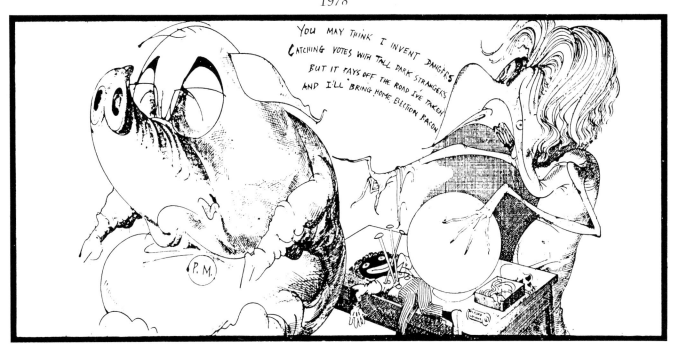

March 5 Callaghan and Thatcher approach the 1978 election. The Tories are accused of a 'bash the immigrants' election campaign. There is talk of reducing immigration.

April 30 Thatcher and the Steel/Callaghan pact. Healey's budget punishes the middle and higher ranges. Will the government be forced to resign on its proposals?

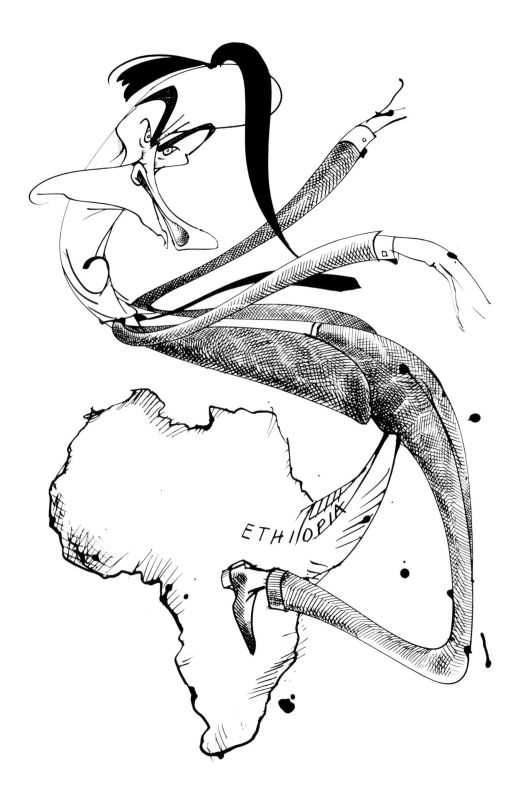

April 9 Dr. David Owen makes a speech at Mansion House about Cuba
and Russian intervention on the Horn of Africa.
The Ethiopian Ambassador walks out.

May 14 Budget defeat because of coalition government. Income tax cuts are forced on the government. The Ulster Unionists join with the Liberals and Scottish Nationalists in supporting the Conservative attempt to cut £500 million off income tax in Mr Healey's budget. Labour says it benefits the rich. Government critics say the tax cuts could by afforded if government waste and bureaucracy were removed. There are calls for the government to go. Thatcher, Powell, Healey and Steel.

June 19 There is certain to be an election in the autumn.

THE AMERICAN EAGLE?
DOVE?
HAWK?

June 11 What kind of beast is President Carter?

August 13 Carter's Middle East peace efforts. Sadat, Carter and Begin are to meet at Camp David on September 5. After a period of bitter estrangement Sadat and Begin are ready to talk. Carter offers a separate Israeli/Egyptian deal divorced from the Palestinian problem. Carter's stock, which is at a low ebb, shoots up.

May 28 David Steel announces the end of the Lib/Lab pact but the Liberals will continue to sustain the government until devolution becomes law. Mrs Thatcher is accused of being too dogmatic, cold and doctrinaire and of being populist when it comes to immigration, law and order and defence. It rests with Powell and the Ulster Unionists whether the government is defeated or not. Thatcher has a brush with the National Front.

September 17 Jeremy Thorpe is acquitted of conspiracy to murder but is disowned by the Liberals, especially Cyril Smith. A diplomat has been murdered by a poisoned umbrella.

September 24 Callaghan clarifies the position for Kaunda. After the embarassment of the sanction-busting oil companies Callaghan flies to visit Kaunda in Kano to discuss the measures to be taken in Southern Africa. Smith asks Callaghan for talks in Rhodesia. After five years of guerilla war the economy is deteriorating so rapidly Smith would like to return to legality.

October 15 Heath and Thatcher are getting on as badly as ever. Heath launches a one-man attack on Mrs Thatcher and her incomes policy at the Brighton Conference but receives little support. Heath has declared support for Callaghan's income policy.

London 1978

Violence
Luvly
Violence

THE ISRAELI WAR MACHINE

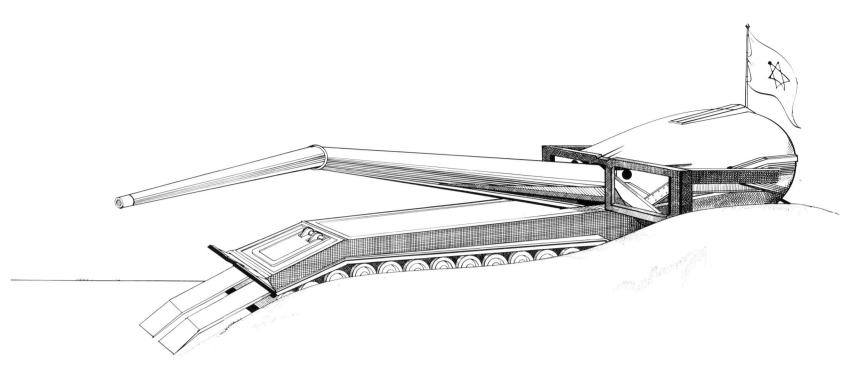

July 9 Menachem Begin of Israel. Middle East flare-up. Lebanon is torn by conflict and the forces of Syria and Israel are on the alert. The Israelis prevent the Syrians from storming Christian-held East Beirut.

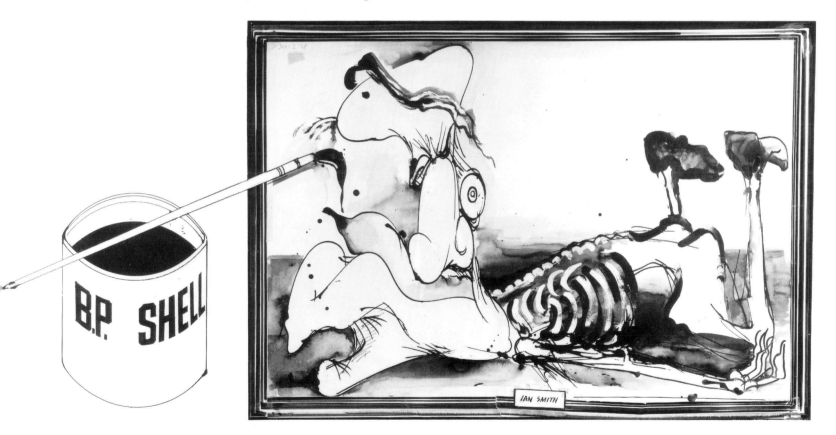

September 3 Forgery in Oil. Ever since Ian Smith made his Unilateral Declaration of Independence in 1965 Britain has believed sanctions were being imposed. Now it has been discovered that Shell and BP have been pouring oil directly or indirectly into Rhodesia.

August 27 Middle East terrorists are active in London. Gun and grenade attacks on the El Al branch office in Mayfair.

October 8 Joe Gormley, with Heath's head on his belt, threatens Callaghan over his 5% wage rise ceiling.

1979

WHO CONTROLS THE COUNTRY?
SIR GEOFFREY HOWE?
AND WHYE?

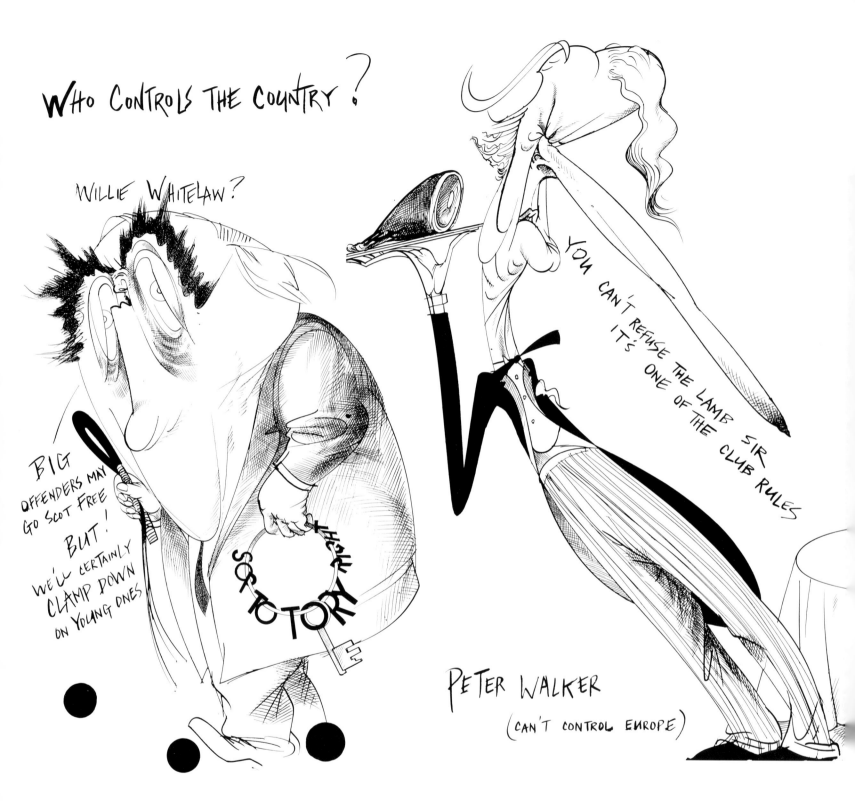

WHO CONTROLS THE COUNTRY?

WILLIE WHITELAW?

BIG OFFENDERS MAY GO SCOT FREE

BUT! WE'LL CERTAINLY CLAMP DOWN ON YOUNG ONES

SCOT TO TORY

YOU CAN'T REFUSE THE LAMB SIR IT'S ONE OF THE CLUB RULES

PETER WALKER

(CAN'T CONTROL EUROPE)

◄ **November 18** Chancellor of the Exchequer Geoffrey Howe after six months is spending more than Denis Healey. In 1978 Healey in replying to a parliamentary attack by Sir Geoffrey Howe said it was rather like being savaged by a dead sheep.

November 18 Peter Walker and Willie Whitelaw, the Tory grandee.

November 25 Mrs Thatcher is made Prime Minister on May 4 and manages her cabinet with an iron hand. Mrs Thatcher takes her cabinet to dinner. 'What will you have?' says the waiter. 'Roast beef,' says Mrs Thatcher. 'What about the vegetables?' says the waiter. 'Oh, they'll have the same as me.' says Mrs Thatcher. Mrs Thatcher says Britain is paying more than her fair share to the EEC

December 9 Teddy Kennedy to run for or from office? He is dogged by the tragedy of Mary Jo Kopechne, the girl who died in his car when it ran off Chapaquiddick Bridge with Kennedy at the wheel.

1980

January 6 Russia invades Afghanistan. Jimmy Carter collapses while jogging. Carter and the Americans boycott the Olympic Games in Moscow in protest against the invasion.

May 18 With the election approaching, Carter is caught in the Afghanistan trap. Senator Edward Muskie appeals to Soviet foreign minister Gromyko while Reagan hovers

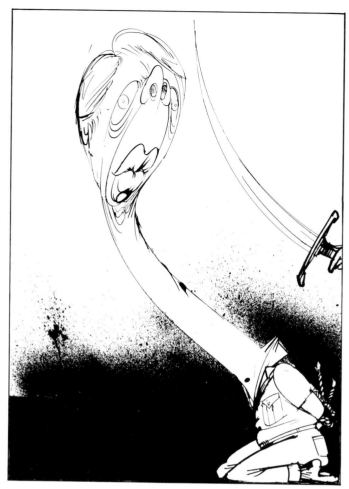

April 13 After the Revolution in Iran, the Shah was in New York undergoing medical treatment. The US Government refused demands for his return, so Muslim militants seized the US embassy in Teheran on November 4, taking the diplomats as hostages. Six months later Carter is in deep trouble as he fails to release them.

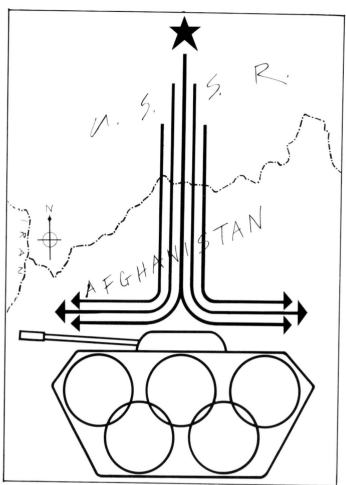

April 20 The Olympic symbol. Russian tanks advance into Afghanistan.

August 10 Jimmy Carter, Peanut Farmer and President, is embarrassed by his beer-swilling brother Billy's connections with Libya.

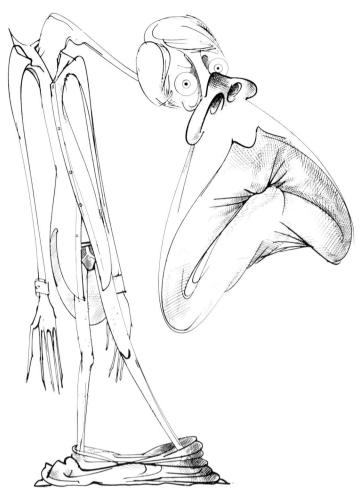

April 27 Carter's desert disaster. He attempts to rescue the hostages. American transport planes and helicopters carrying 90 commandos take off from Egypt and fly to a deserted airstrip in Iran. When the rescue bid starts some of the helicopters collided with the planes. Commandos were killed and their leader abandoned the operation.

May 25 Brezhnev and Carter and the Olympic fiasco

August 3 The question is being asked: Is Carter the worst President since the war?

▼

THE DUNKIRK SPIRIT

H.M.S. SALVAGE WHAT YOU CAN

£720 MILLION

£860 MILLION

5% FARM PRICE RISE

June 1 Lord Carrington, the Foreign Secretary, and Mrs Thatcher escape with what they can from Europe. The EEC Council of Ministers agree to massive reductions in Britain's budget contributions. Giscard d'Estaing looks on.

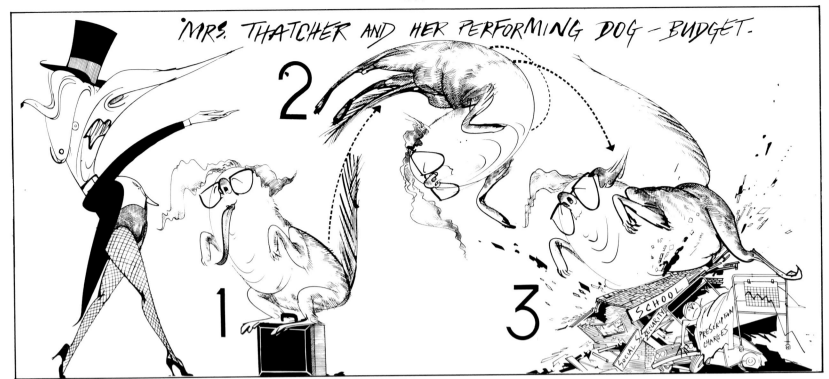

March 30 Sir Geoffrey Howe, Chancellor of Exchequer, performs somersaults and comes down hard on schools and hospitals. The Chancellor's dog is called Budget.

July 27 2,000,000 people are now without work

August 31 Mrs Thatcher is determined to make her policies work.

July 6 Keith Joseph and Mrs Thatcher. The unemployment level is the highest since the war. The musical *Sweeney Todd* opens in London.

June 8 Wedgwood Benn feels that Callaghan is steering the Labour ▶
Party too much to the right and it is time he went. Benn talks of the
refounding of the Labour Party and becoming the next Leader but
he is still regarded with suspicion within the Party. There is a 'stop
Benn' campaign.

◀ **September 28** Callaghan and the unions. The Labour Party at
Blackpool is in a mess. Conflict between Left and Right about the
constitution. Conflict in the contest to succeed Callaghan and
conflict within the TUC itself.

BIG BENN
TRIES TO TELL CINDERS
HE'S BEEN TOO LONG
AT THE BALL s

August 24 The people of Poland go on strike under Russian oppression.

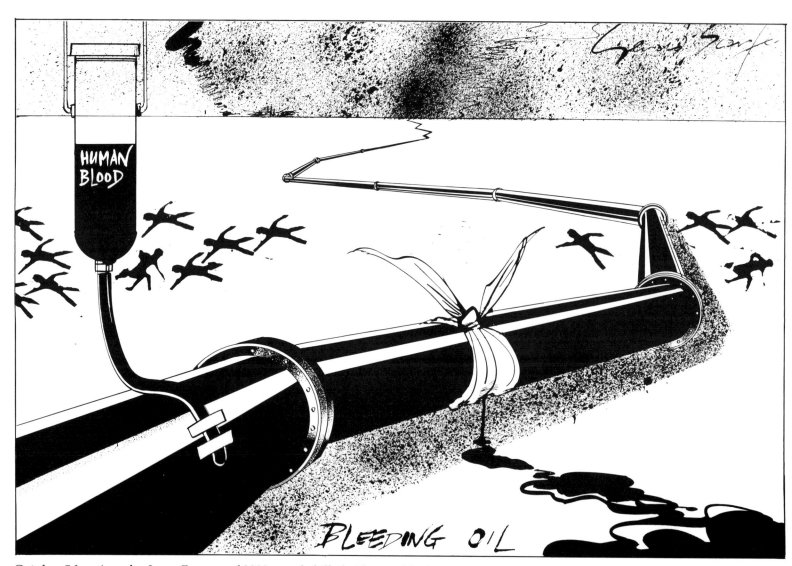

October 5 Iraq invades Iran. Reports of 2000 people killed. The world's biggest oil refinery is on fire - oil supplies are threatened.

October 12 The Conservative Party Conference at Brighton. Unemployment at the highest level since the war. Mrs Thatcher says, 'The lady's not for turning.'

July 20 Ronald Reagan and his running mate George Bush prepare for the election.

POINT OF BALANCE

November 2 The American Elections. Carter is worried by the invasion of Afghanistan and the fact he is unable to release the 52 hostages held by radical students in Iran even after 364 days. Reagan is still singing the praises of the arms race.
There are fears that he might increase the defence budget, review the B1 bomber and neutron bomb which Carter put aside.

November 9 Reagan elected President of the USA.

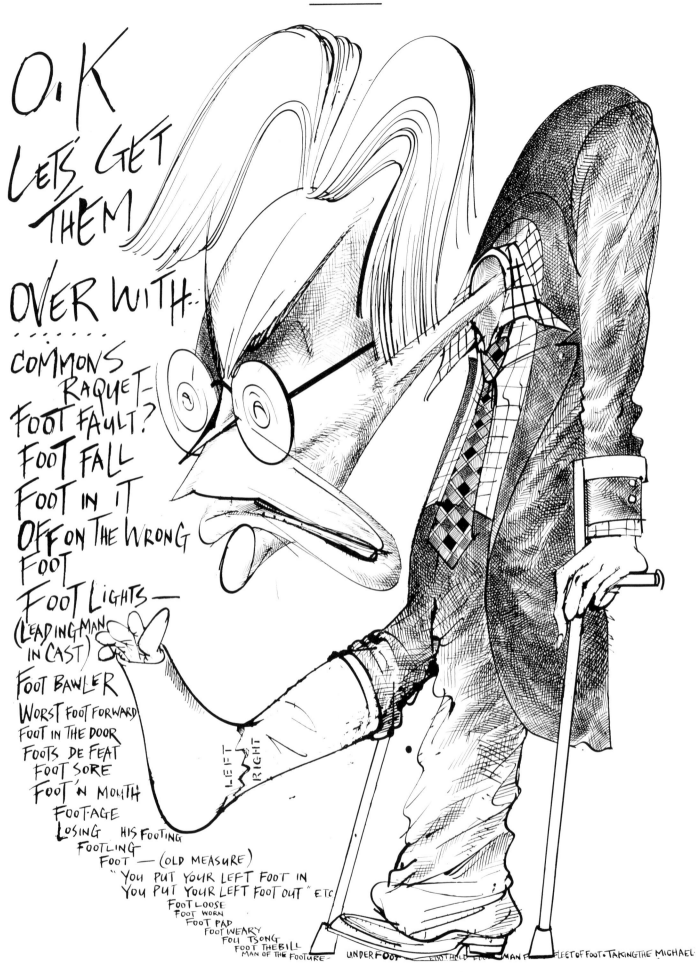

O.K
LETS GET
THEM

OVER WITH..

COMMONS
RAQUET-
FOOT FAULT?
FOOT FALL
FOOT IN IT
OFF ON THE WRONG
FOOT
FOOT LIGHTS —
(LEADING MAN
IN CAST)

FOOT BAWLER
WORST FOOT FORWARD
FOOT IN THE DOOR
FOOTS DE FEAT
FOOT SORE
FOOT 'N MOUTH
FOOT·AGE
LOSING HIS FOOTING
FOOTLING
FOOT — (OLD MEASURE)
"YOU PUT YOUR LEFT FOOT IN
YOU PUT YOUR LEFT FOOT OUT" ETC
FOOT LOOSE
FOOT WORN
FOOT PAD
FOOT WEARY
FOU TSONG
FOOT THE BILL
MAN OF THE FOOTURE UNDER FOOT FOOTHOLD FOOT MAN FLEET OF FOOT·TAKING THE MICHAEL

LEFT RIGHT

November 16 Michael Foot (who has broken his foot) elected leader of Labour Party.

November 30 Britain is experiencing the worst recession of the century. Despite her Keynesian critics Mrs Thatcher sticks to her monetary policies. Sir Geoffrey Howe (being dragged behind) is not one of Mrs Thatcher's intimate counsellors but very much under her thumb. Mrs Thatcher's mentor is Sir Keith Joseph.

December 21 Happy Christmas.

1981

KILL KILL KILL!

FIGURE OF JUSTICE 1981

DR. FROWENSTEIN TO CREATE NEW MONSTER!

January 25 Doctor Frowenstein. Dr David Owen is about to form
the Social Democratic Party, a new party left of centre, hoping to
seize the middle ground.

◄ **October 11** Terrorism.

I ALWAYS THIS MOMENT IN A PARTY WHEN YOU WONDER IF ANYONE WILL TURN UP

C.S.D.

February 15 The Social Democrats are to be formed: Roy Jenkins, William Rodgers, Dr David Owen and Shirley Williams. The 'Gang of Four' are pro-European, favouring the mixed economy.

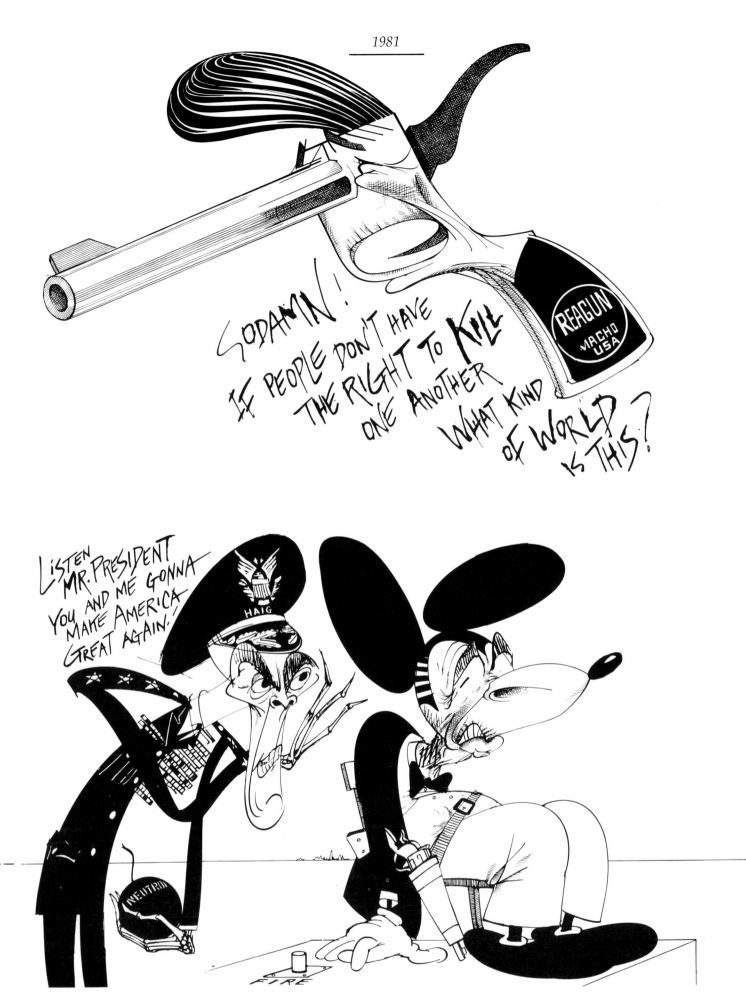

February 8 General Haig encourages the newly elected Reagan. Reagan talks tough, calling the Soviets cheats and liars and accusing them of terrorism. Defence Secretary Weinberger brandishes the neutron bomb at a press conference.

March 8 Ronald Reagan

March 22 Thatcher meets West Germany's Helmut Schmidt head-on in Maastricht on the issue of fishing rights at the thrice-yearly EEC summit. There are deep gulfs between Britain and the EEC on many matters. Britain wants to hang on to her fishing rights. There are niggles over Canadian cod and Cornish mackerel.

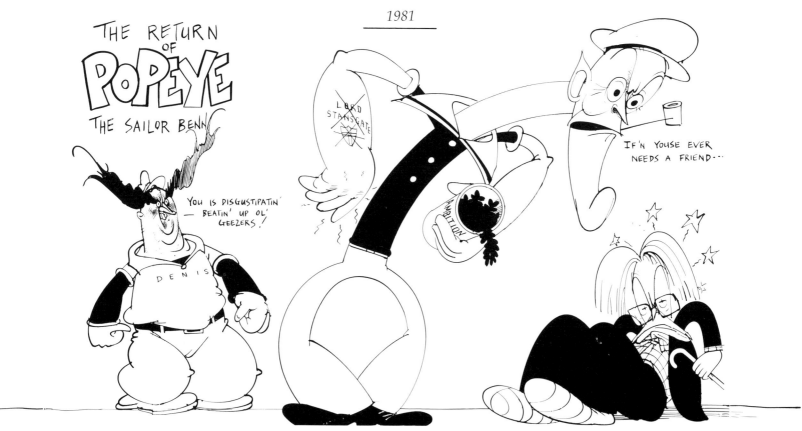

THE RETURN OF POPEYE THE SAILOR BENN

YOU IS DISGUSTIPATIN' — BEATIN' UP OL' GEEZERS!

DENIS

LORD STANSGATE

AMBITION

IF'N YOUSE EVER NEEDS A FRIEND---

May 24 Wedgwood Benn attacks Foot again. The onward march of the new Left led by Tony Benn. Foot calls him a man of 'fatally suspect integrity'. Labour's Democratic Left consider him a menace to Labour's chance of victory in the polls. Mr Healey is on the Party's Right.

IT WASN'T LIKE THIS IN MY DAY

SIR HAROLD

MEDICAL REPORT
LABOUR PARTY

September 6 Harold Wilson muses on the in-fighting in the Labour Party for the Deputy Leadership. Confidential medical documents are found on a rubbish heap.

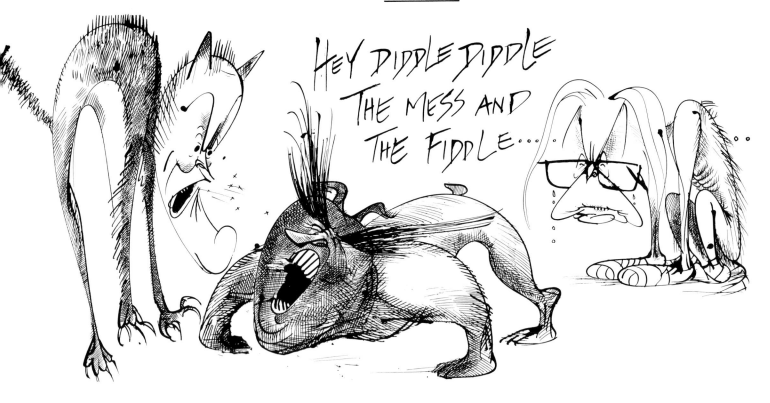

HEY DIDDLE DIDDLE
THE MESS AND
THE FIDDLE...

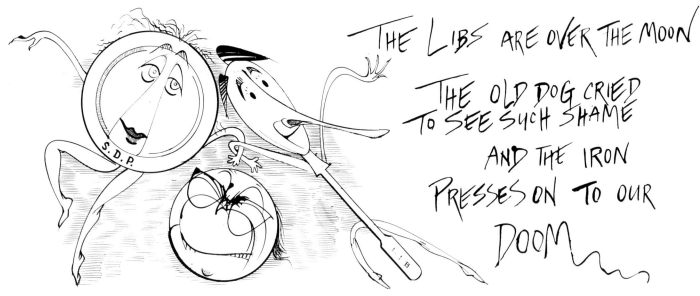

THE LIBS ARE OVER THE MOON

THE OLD DOG CRIED
TO SEE SUCH SHAME

AND THE IRON
PRESSES ON TO OUR
DOOM

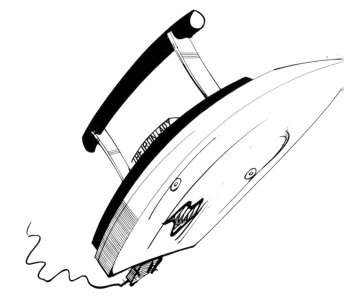

September 20 The state of the parties. Labour's Deputy Leadership fight between Wedgwood Benn and Denis Healey. The Liberals have joined with the SDP and are doing well. The Iron Lady presses on.

August 23 Northern Ireland. Over 2,000 lives have been lost and thousands more have been ruined by bereavement or mutilation, and there is still no solution.

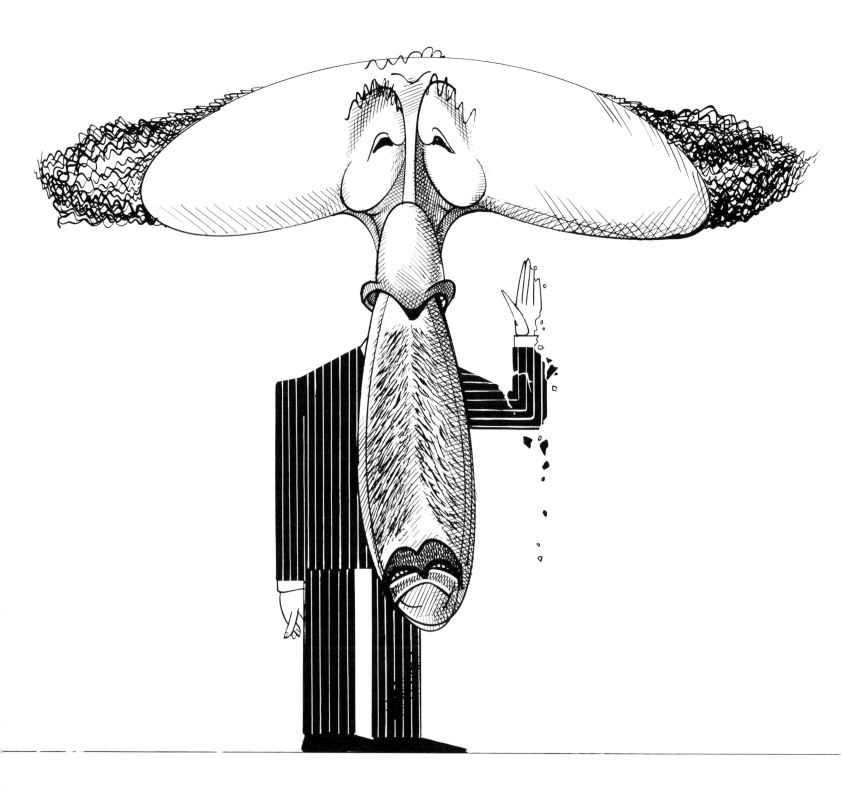

September 13 President Sadat's high hopes of peace at Camp David have begun to founder and crack. Sadat is murdered in October.

BEGIN IN AGAIN — THE OLD BUZZARD RETURNS TO HIS PERCH.

JINGO SEED

BEWARE BAD LANGUAGE

@*** THE LEBANESE.! SYRIANS ARE *.!@*.!!! BOMB THE @**IRAQUIS.

RELIGIOUS PARTIES

Gerald Scarfe

July 5 Menachem Begin. Israel's dead-heat election leaves the country divided and unsure. Ethnic differences flare.

THE DE-CREATION OF MAN BY REAGAN
APOLOGIES TO MICHELANGELO AND WALT DISNEY
AND MANKIND.

August 16 Ronald Reagan continues his toughness towards the USSR with a vastly-increased defence budget of $100 billion. Without consulting his allies he goes ahead with the neutron bomb, an alternative warhead for short-range weapons.

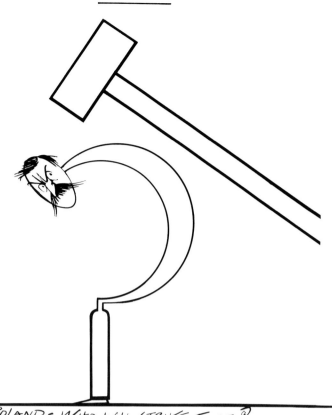

POLAND - WHO WILL STRIKE FIRST ?

March 29 Poland. Lech Welensa, leader of Solidarity's campaign
for a free trade union movement, calls strikes.

Poland. The new freedom.

December 20 Poland. The apparently new-found freedoms are soon curtailed.

1982

April 11 General Alexander Haig, US Secretary of State, Mrs Thatcher and John Nott, Minister of Defence, confront General Galtieri of Argentina.

◄ **November 14** The new Russian Bear: Brezhnev dies and Mr Andropov takes over. What will happen in Russia after Brezhnev?

May 23 The face that launched the Task Force. Under General Galtieri Argentina invades and seizes control of the British-administered Falkland Islands, known as the Malvinas to the Argentinians, who have always considered them part of Argentina. Mrs Thatcher sets sail with the task force for war in the Falklands and sets up a blockade, with a 200-mile limit. The Argentinian ship the Belgrano is sunk with loss of life - some say she was outside the limit and was heading away. Tam Dalyell claims that Mrs Thatcher sank the Belgrano to wreck the Peruvian initiative. ▶

June 20 Mrs Thatcher is overjoyed with her Falklands victory despite increasing troubles back at home, not least who pays for the war.

THE
FALKLANDS
1982

NEW
FOLLY
PROPOSED
ON THIS
SITE
£100 MILLION

September 19 Can Mrs Thatcher solve the despondent domestic scene with the same immediacy as she did the Falklands? The maintaining of the Falklands will cost £100 million, including a new runway for planes.

September 26 Begin and the Phalangists. Massacre in Beirut. Israel denies prior knowledge.

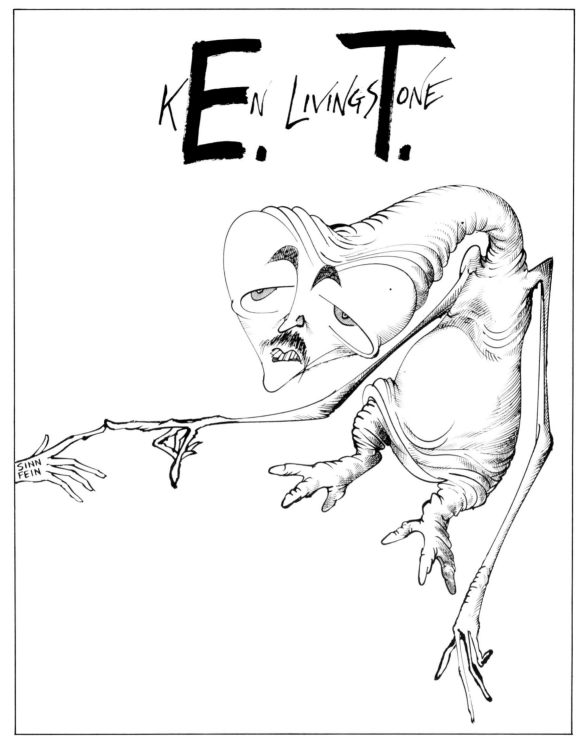

December 12 Ken Livingstone, the Greater London Council leader, causes fury by inviting Sinn Fein leaders to meet him in London. There is a bombing in Ballykelly in which 17 die. E.T. is a popular film about an alien creature.

December 5 Mrs Thatcher - many are unemployed in the steel industry.

1983

January 2 The New Year.

◄ **May 29** Michael Foot. Despite a disastrous week for the Tories,
with leaked government documents and embarrassing trade
figures, Labour manages to shoot itself on its policy over Polaris
missiles. After a commitment that Britain would become the first
nuclear weapons state to renounce unilaterally such weapons,
Labour begins to hedge on the issue of Polaris.

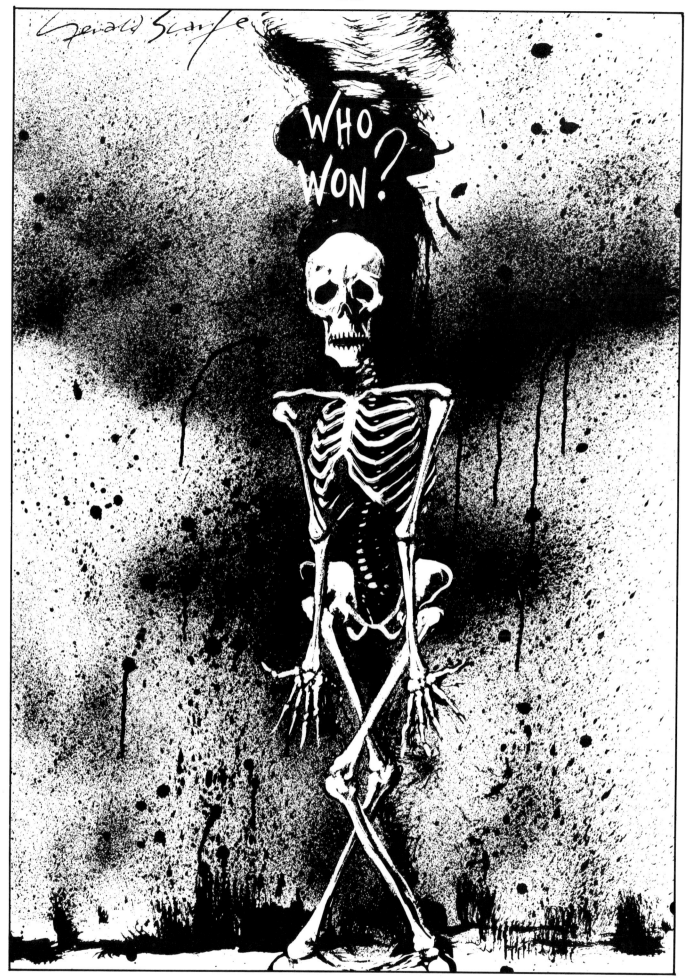

March 13 Nuclear War.

March 27 Out of the gloom, while the pound plunges, Labour wins Darlington by-election. Michael Foot as the Rocket.

August 21 A four-legged friend - he'll never let you down. Will Ronald Reagan run again for the Presidency? Older by two years than anyone who ever held the office, Reagan reigns over a country with more people below the poverty line than at any time since LBJ.

June 26 The Pope visits his home country.
General Jaruzelski's Soviet-controlled Poland.

May 8 Andropov, the Russian leader who died soon after his election.

UGH! LOOKS LIKE MORE MEDICINE

◀ **June 5** Election Fever: Nanny Thatcher. It looks as though Mrs Thatcher will win the election. There is a fall in Labour support. Mrs Thatcher's tendency to believe only she is right, and that anyone who disagrees with her is automatically wrong, is well known. She is the least admired Prime Minister in the history of opinion polls, but the Labour shambles under Michael Foot, and the Falklands, assure her win.

June 12 Mrs Thatcher wins the election, her parliamentary majority trebled - yet her share of the popular vote has diminished. The Alliance, who tapped the vein of anti-extremism, has a low ratio of seats to votes. There is a strong case for proportional representation. ▶

October 16 At the Blackpool conference Cecil Parkinson, the Industry Secretary, puts on a brave front when his secretary Sarah Keays discloses that she is carrying his baby, but when an interview with her in *The Times* reveals that he lied to her and to Mrs Thatcher he is dismissed from the cabinet. (Don't worry - he'll be back in 1988 as Chairman of the Star Chamber and possible future Chancellor of the Exchequer.)

POWER

TROOPING THE COLOUR

July 3 Francis Pym, the Foreign Secretary, cautions compassion for the needy and unemployed. He is sacked and later writes a critical analysis of Mrs Thatcher.

August 29 Farewell Welfare. Crisis over public spending. The collapse of the health service, cuts in the dole, etc. Mrs Thatcher decimates the welfare state.

December 18 Len Murray, the TUC General Secretary. The TUC decide not to back the National Graphical Association in its closed shop dispute with Eddie Shah and his use of non-union labour to produce newspapers in Warrington. Union picketing fails to move Shah, and fines for contempt mount. The NGA decide to call a 24-hour national strike, with backing from the TUC, but the TUC decide to live within the law of the land.

1984

March 4 My view of Mrs Thatcher in her fifth year of office, as an ice-box on rails. Mrs Thatcher bans the unions at GCHQ, Cheltenham, and her opponents accuse her of dictatorial tendencies and inflexibility. They think she has made a bad job of employment, the health service and electricity prices.

July 29 Sir Geoffrey Howe and the handing over by the British of Hong Kong to China in 1997.

July 15 Mrs Thatcher puts on a cheerful face

April 29 A 1984 nightmare - could Ghadaffi get the bomb?

Another Extremely Important Person Found in a Diplomatic Bag

July 8 Arthur Scargill has called a national miners' strike without a ballot but a third of Britain's coalfields decide they want a ballot first. There are calls to democratise the unions. A new act, requiring ballots for strikes, becomes law. Scargill is determined to fight back against what he sees as the destruction of British industry, the decimation of jobs and the death of communities. Ian MacGregor is the trouble-shooter for the Coal Board. The former Nigerian transport minister, Umaru Dikko, is found being smuggled, against his will, in a cargo box at Heathrow, bound for Lagos.

July 22 Frozen embryos. A debate on the moral implications and fears about cloning.

SURROGATE MOTHER

August 5 Ken Livingstone, Leader of the GLC, must hand his baby over to the government.
Many oppose abolition of the Greater London Council, including surprisingly, the House of
Lords. Surrogate mothers are a current issue.

September 23 Leaks in the Civil Service. The government seems plagued by leaks: leaked papers on welfare payments, on a 45p tax rate, on Cruise missiles, budget leaks, leaks on Thatcher and the pay talks, and leaked papers on the sinking of the Belgrano (Clive Ponting is charged).

October 7 Considering the atrocious levels of unemployment, Labour's standing in the opinion polls is amazingly low. They cannot seem to deliver a death blow. At the Blackpool Labour conference, Kinnock, Labour Leader after one year, is outshone by Scargill. The coal war is now in its seventh month.

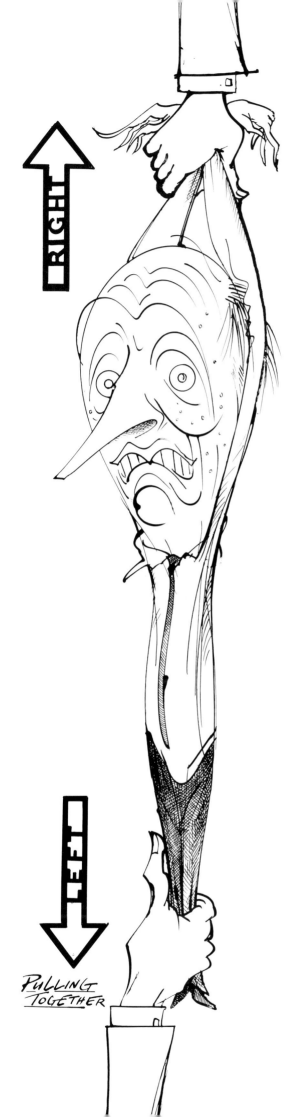

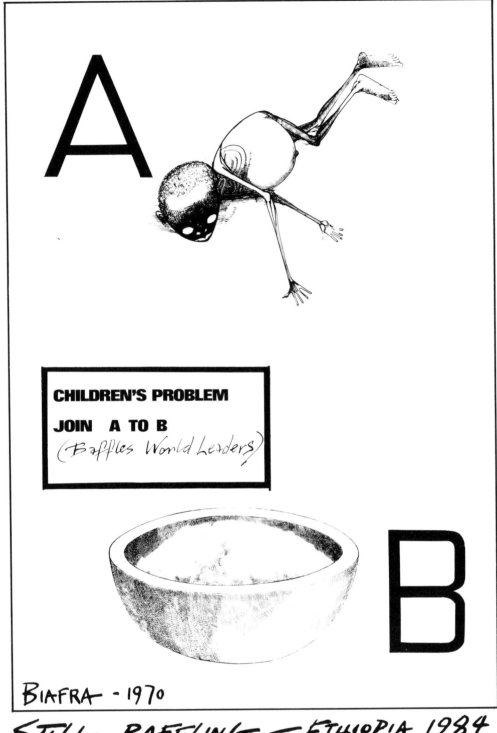

CHILDREN'S PROBLEM

JOIN A TO B

(Baffles World Leaders)

BIAFRA - 1970

STILL BAFFLING — ETHIOPIA 1984

October 28 A terrible famine in Ethiopia. Reprint of a 1970 cartoon, still applicable 15 years later.

December 16 The coal talks go round in circles. The Secretary of State for ▶ Energy, Peter Walker, the Tory wet who has been put in charge of negotiations by Mrs Thatcher, and TUC leader Norman Willis. Scargill has visited Libya to obtain financial support for the miners. The strike is in its death throes. There are healthy stocks of coal at the pithead and in the power stations, and the TUC and Labour leadership are not rallying to the Scargill cause. 5,000 strikers return to work.

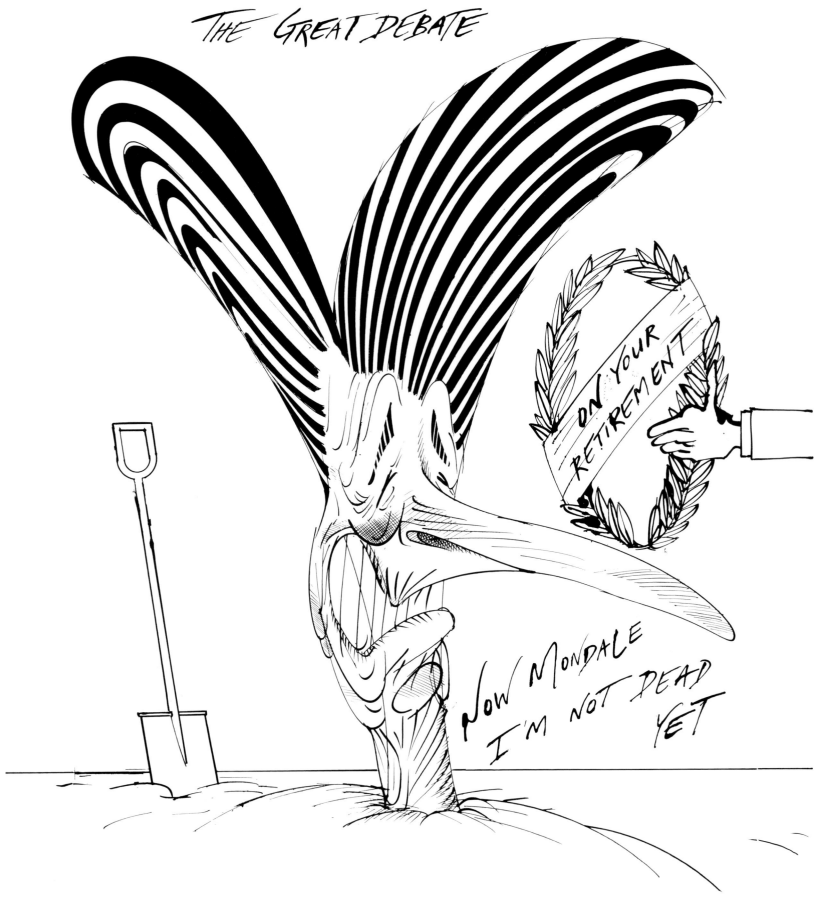

THE GREAT DEBATE

ON YOUR RETIREMENT

NOW MONDALE I'M NOT DEAD YET

October 21 Presidential elections. There is a television debate between the Democrat Walter Mondale and Ronald Reagan. Mondale chooses a woman running mate, Congresswoman Geraldine Ferraro. The business activities of her husband come under attack and she drops out. Reagan is re-elected.

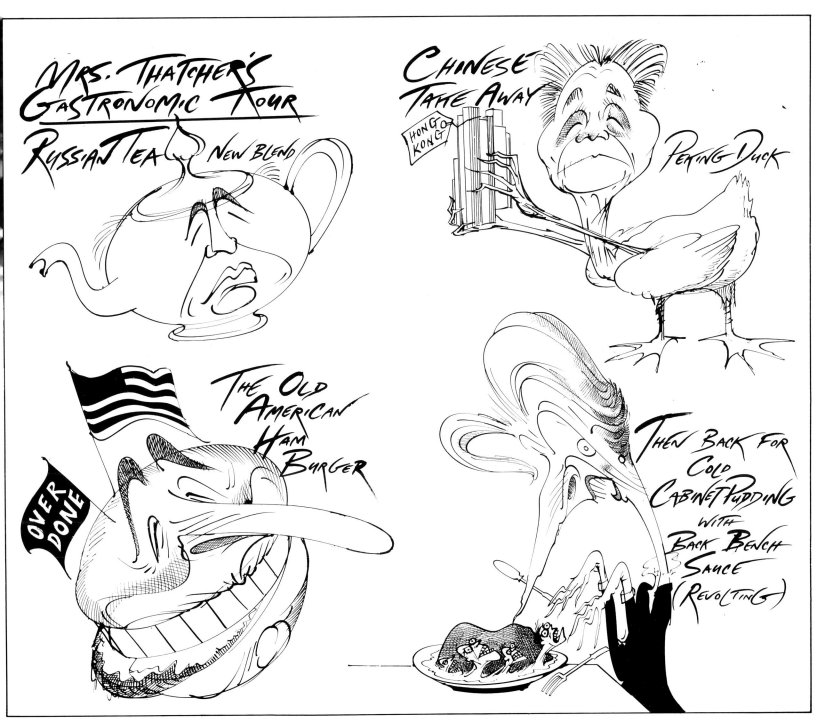

December 23 Mrs Thatcher circumnavigates the world in 130 hours, meeting the fast-rising Mikhail Gorbachev at Chequers and President Reagan at Camp David. Reagan wins a landslide re-election and promises to try to eliminate nuclear weaons in his second term. Mrs Thatcher goes on to a meeting with Chinese leader Deng Xiaoping in Peking.

UNEMPLOYMENT

HE SEEMS TO BE HANGING AROUND THIS YEAR –

1985

December 30 Nigel Lawson, the Chancellor of the Exchequer, promises tax reform and tax reduction.

1985

February 17 Gorbachev elected in Moscow. Under Brezhnev there was corruption and complacency. The new vigorous Russian leader looks like a new broom. At the funeral of the short-lived President Chernenko, Gorbachev orders the National Anthem to be played at a brisk marching pace as though to hasten an old era on its way.

March 24 At Langa South African police fire live ammunition into a crowd of 4,000 people who ▶ are commemorating Sharpeville.

◀ **September 22** Dr David Owen and David Steel. The SDP-Liberal alliance looks in its best shape yet, triumphing at its conference. However the two Davids do not get on too well.

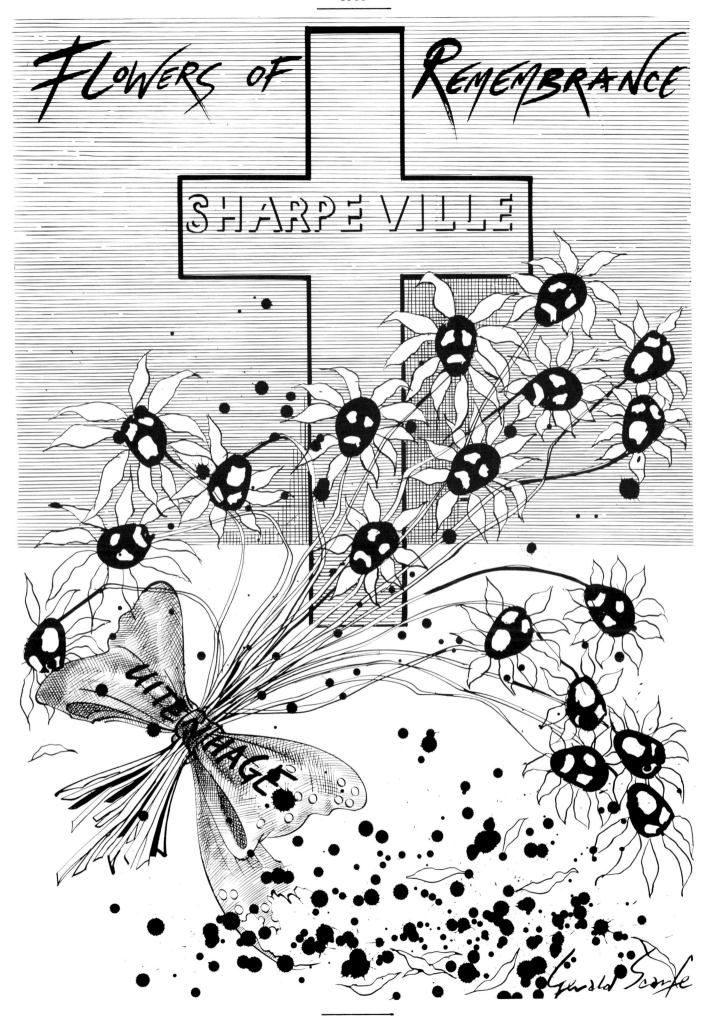

February 24 Thatcher and Reagan - the dollar squeezes the pound. Another surge in the dollar brings a succession of record pound-dollar lows. Mrs Thatcher must convince the world that sterling is more than a petrol currency; when oil prices slip, so does sterling.

June 23 Reagan and the White House struggle impotently to find a way to free the hijack hostages ▶ held by the Shi'ites in the Lebanon.

THE AMERICAN EAGLE

BEWARE THATCHERWOCKY

July 7 It is Wimbledon fortnight. Mrs Thatcher, as the volatile tennis player John McEnroe, loses disastrously in the Brecon and Radnorshire by-election. The polls had predicted a Labour landslide but the Alliance take the lion's share of the Tory dissenters.

◄ **May 5** Thatcher and Owen fight it out in the county elections. The SDP-Liberal alliance is poised for what could be a break-through. The Conservatives lose in county halls across the country. They have failed to reduce unemployment.

June 16 A TWA plane flying from Cairo to Rome makes a stop in Athens, where a Shi'ite hijacker boards. He tortures and kills an American.

November 3 Ronald Reagan. Americans, say, 'Who cares if Reagan doesn't understand the Beirut thing or the deficit thing, he's Uncle Sam.' The most powerful nation in the world for years, humiliated and impotent in the face of Middle East hijackers and bombers, has hit back.

June 30 Terrorism continues across the world.

THE NEW JOHN BULL

June 2 Football hooligan. 38 are killed and more than 250 injured at the European cup final in
Brussels, when rioting Liverpool fans surge forward, crushing those in front to death against a wall.

1986

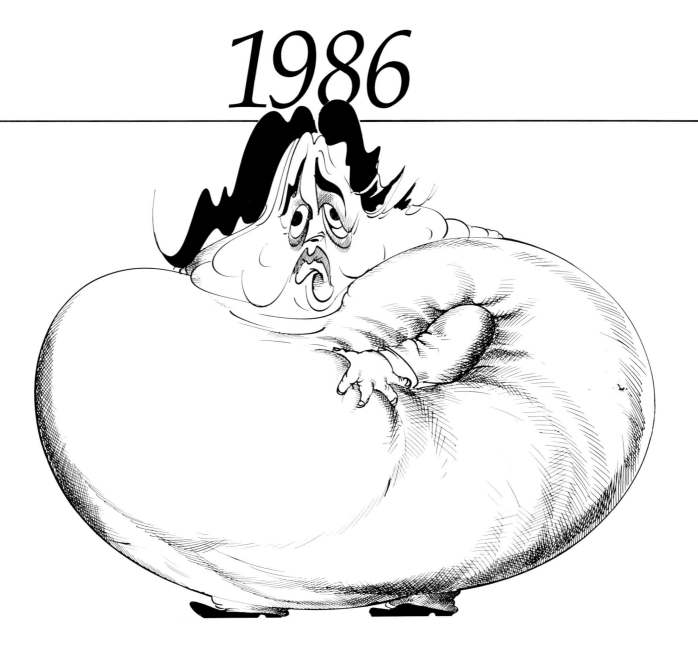

FIGHTING
INFLATION

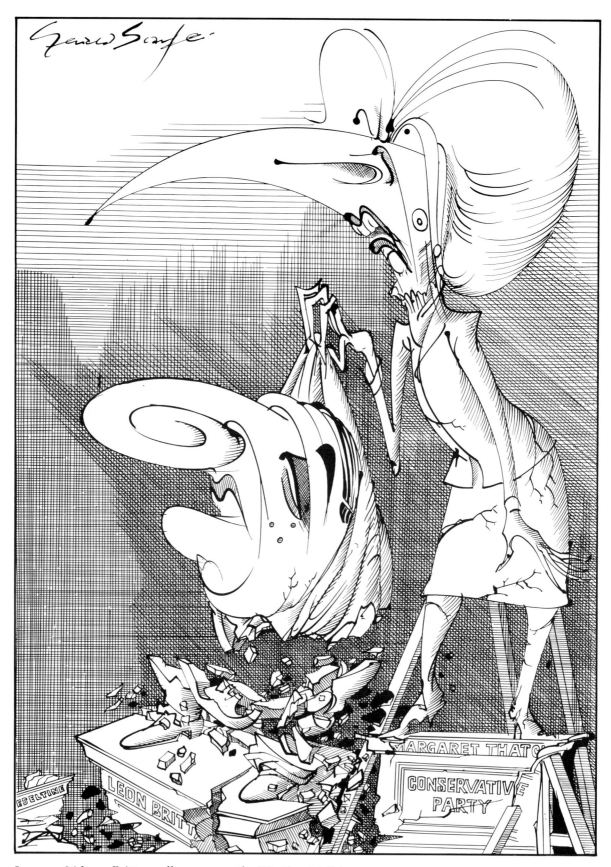

January 26 Leon Brittan collapses over the Westland Affair.

◀ **October 19** Nigel Lawson, Chancellor of the Exchequer.

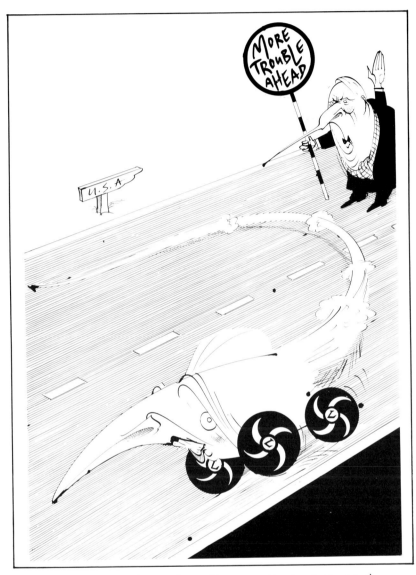

February 9 Mrs Thatcher makes a U-turn on Leyland. Ford is in negotiation with Leyland for a take-over. The cabinet saves Austin Rover for the nation.

July 13 Sir Geoffrey Howe shuttles between Lusaka and Harare, looking for a peaceful solution to South African problems, in the hope of boosting Mrs Thatcher's morale. Leon Brittan, the scapegoat of the Westland affair, says, 'What kind of bargaining power will Sir Geoffrey have if we continue making it plain to President Botha that South Africa has little to fear from us in the way of sanctions?'

February 23 Nuclear Power.

April 6 Innocents suffer in bomb outrages.

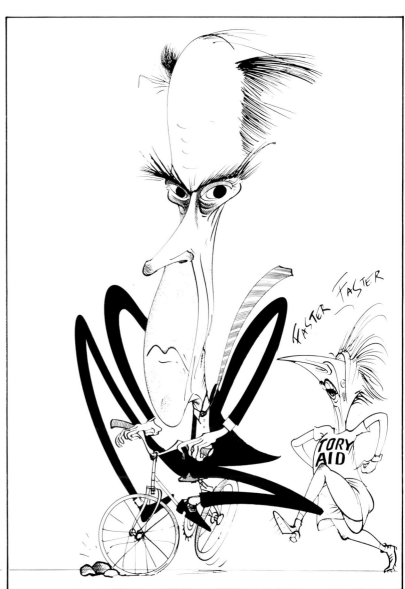

April 27 Margaret Thatcher feels she has supported the US with its bombing of Libya. American tourists stay away from Britain this year because of Libyan-inspired bomb threats.

May 18 Norman Tebbit's catch phrase to encourage the unemployed was: 'On your Bike', Mrs Thatcher's hit man, known as the Chingford skinhead and the unspeakable Tebbit, has had a meteoric rise.

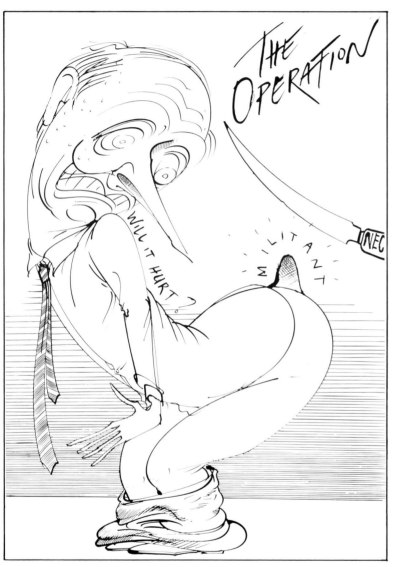

March 2 Neil Kinnock tries to purge the ultra Left-wing faction Militant from the Labour Party

June 1 Neil Kinnock has an unexpected rise in the opinion polls. Times are bad for Mrs Thatcher. The government has slipped on a number of banana skins: Westland, Landrover, British Leyland and John Biffen, who questions Mrs Thatcher's singular style of leadership. Shipyard redundancies are rising, unemployment, cuts in aid for jobless house-owners. Labour is pledged to cancel Trident, decommission on Polaris and expel Cruise missiles from British soil. However the polls say this would be a vote-loser.

October 20 Britannia 1986 ▶

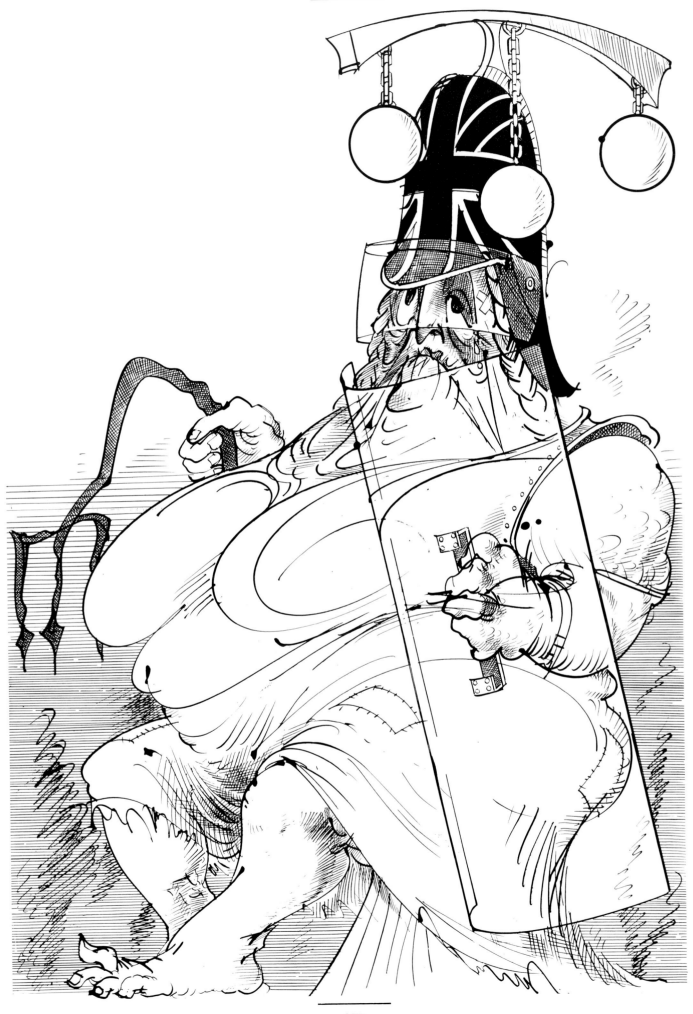

LAME
DUCK
PRESIDENT?

March 23 Reagan requests an increased defence budget to finance the Star Wars project.
The Federal District Court rules that a budget deficit is illegal under the Constitution.

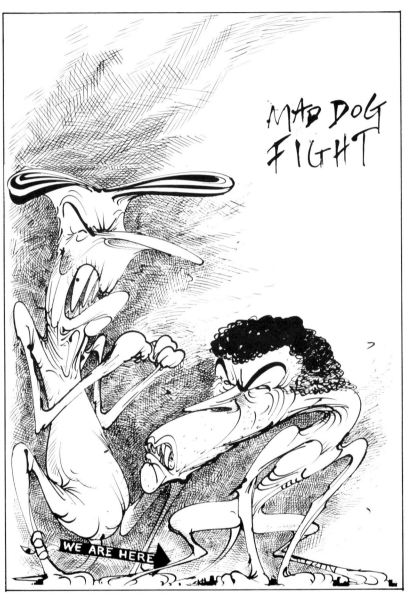

April 13 Reagan bombs Libya. Mrs Thatcher is seen as Reagan's poodle when she allows the bombers to fly from Britain.

July 27 Reagan and Thatcher are alone in refusing to use sanctions against South Africa. The Commonwealth Games are in doubt.

May 11 Nuclear Power - Man's Best Friend.

◄ **May 4** The world's worst nuclear accident happens in Chernobyl, in the Ukraine. The Soviet Union suppresses the news until three days later, 800 miles away in Sweden, steep increases of radiation are recorded. A cloud of poisonous radiation sweeps across Europe.

TURKEY ESCAPES THANKSGIVING

BUT

CHRISTMAS IS COMING.

November 30 The Iran Contra scandal. Reagan is under strong criticism; his policy of secret gun-running to Iran, arms for hostages and illicit money laundering to the Nicaraguan rebels behind the back of Congress. The President's men have diverted the proceeds from the sale of arms to Iran to fund the 'Contras' fighting the left-wing government of Nicaragua despite the wish of Congress that no military aid should be sent to the Contras.

October 26 Gorbachev and Reagan, at a meeting in Reykjavik.

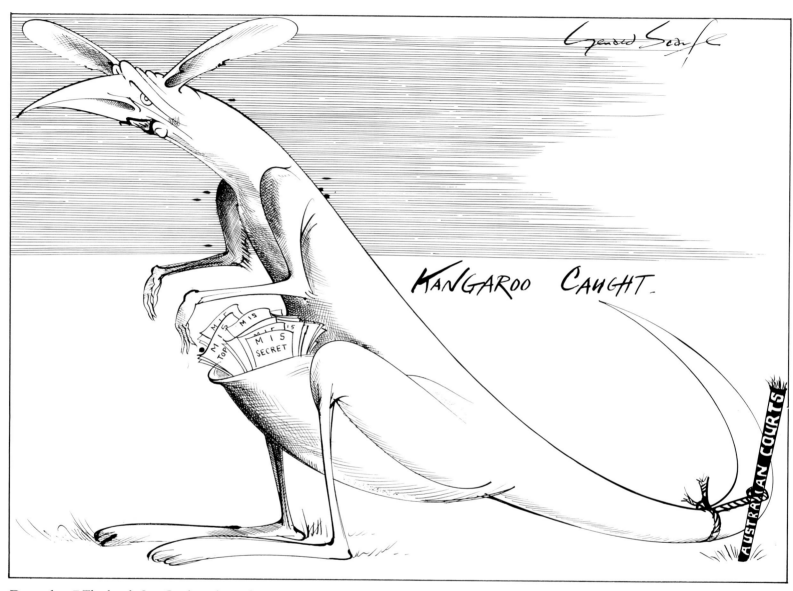

KANGAROO CAUGHT.

December 7 The book *Spy-Catcher*, about the secret service, written by ex-M15 agent Peter Wright, is banned in Britain by Mrs Thatcher. An Australian court, however, rules that Australians can read it. The book claims that M15 officers tried to de-stabilise Wilson's government in 1974-75. Mrs Thatcher refuses an independent inquiry into the allegation.

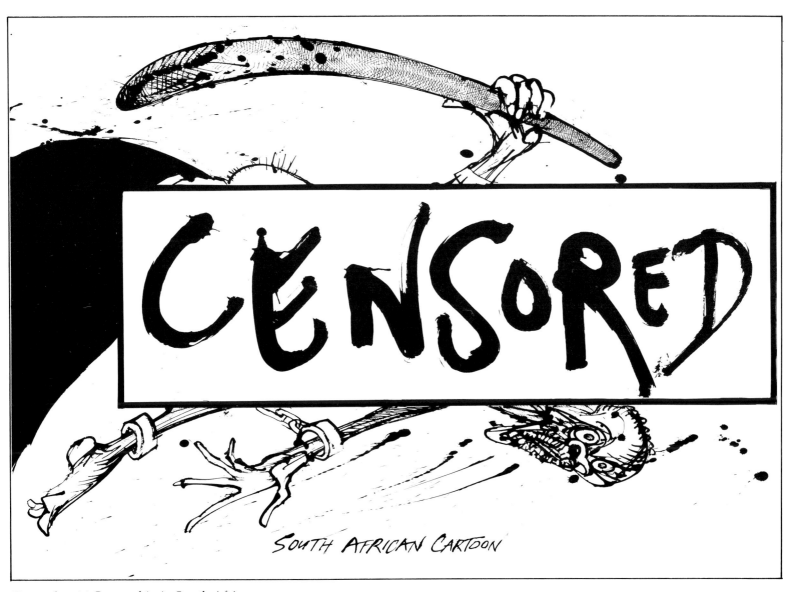

SOUTH AFRICAN CARTOON

December 14 Censorship in South Africa.

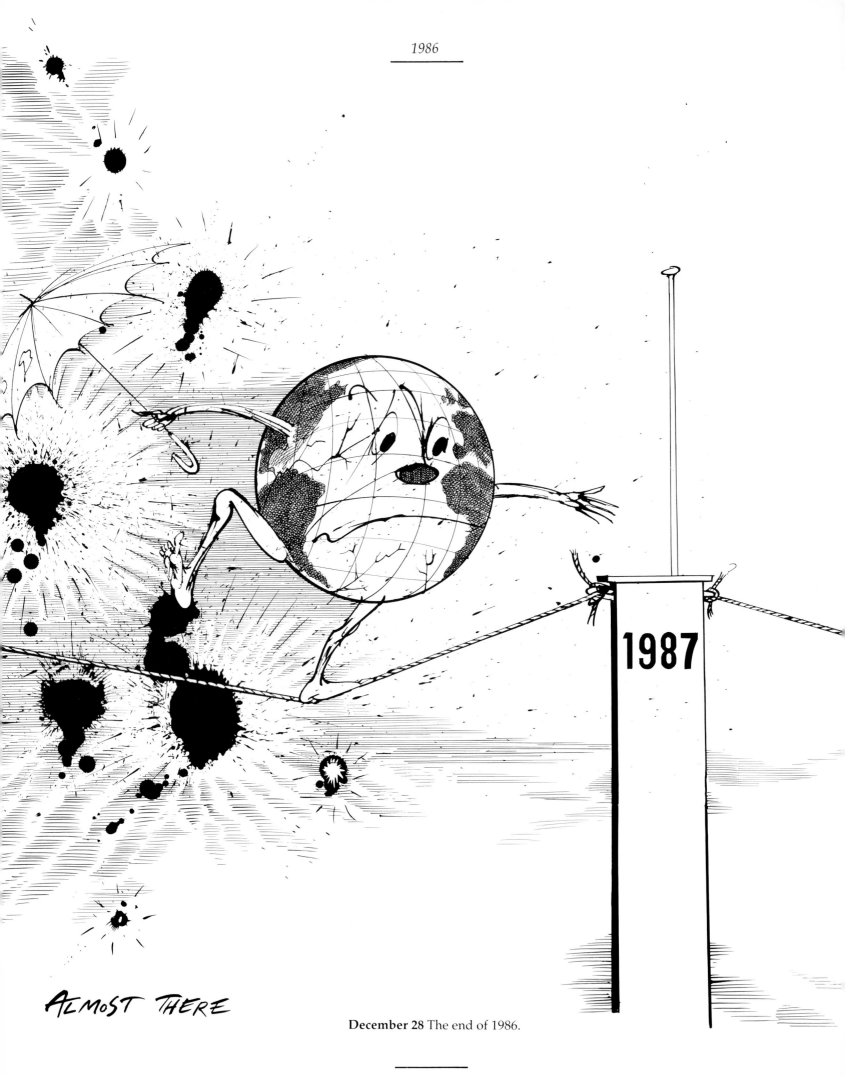

ALMOST THERE

December 28 The end of 1986.

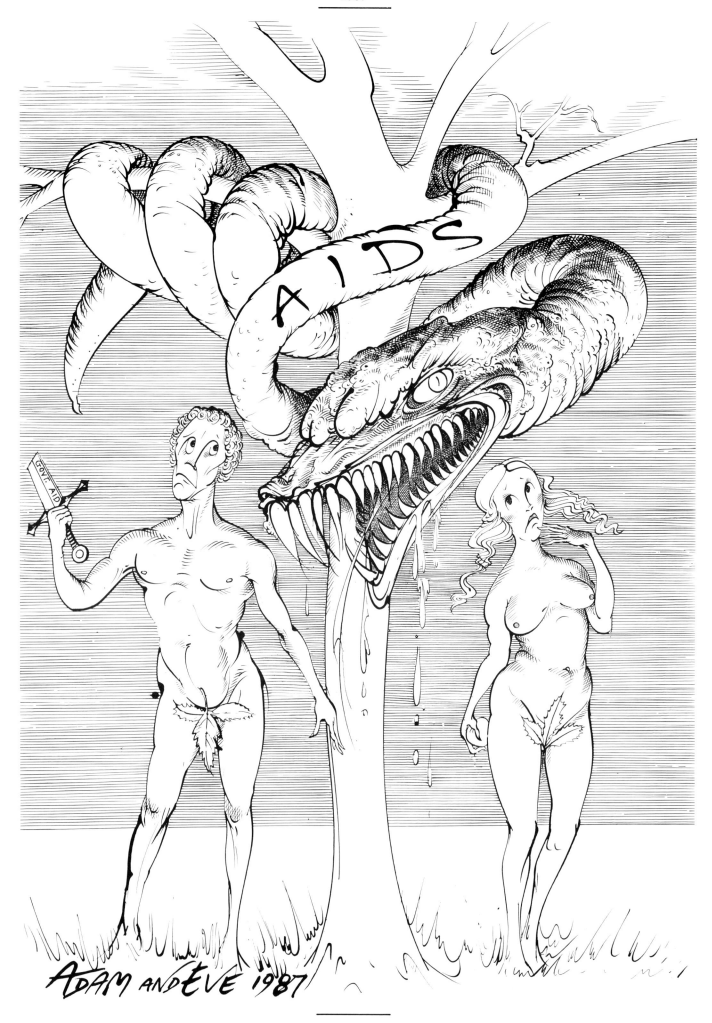

ADAM AND EVE 1987

February 15 Edwina Currie, Junior Minister of Health, and the government programme to promote condoms in the fight against AIDS. She has made herself a national figure by her outspoken comments.

◄ **February 8** AIDS.

◄ ◄ **August 16** The book burner. *Spy-Catcher* is published in Australia and the United States - the government fights in courts around the world to ban it.

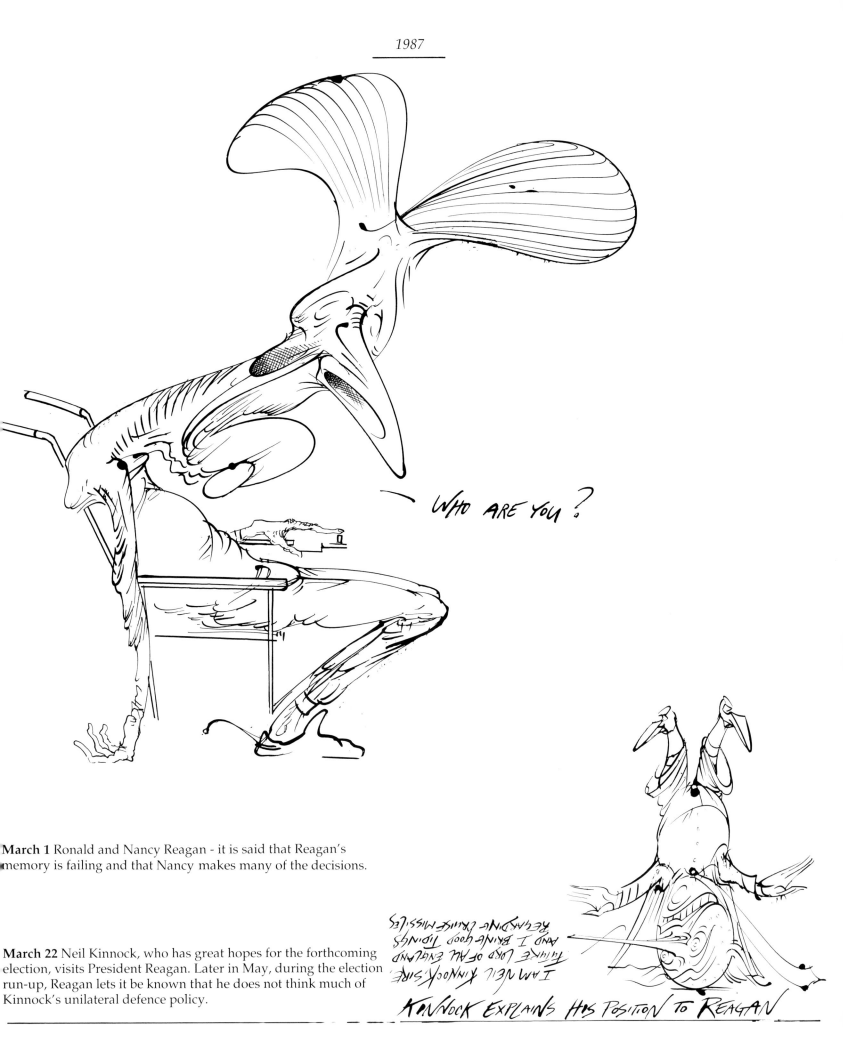

WHO ARE YOU ?

March 1 Ronald and Nancy Reagan - it is said that Reagan's memory is failing and that Nancy makes many of the decisions.

March 22 Neil Kinnock, who has great hopes for the forthcoming election, visits President Reagan. Later in May, during the election run-up, Reagan lets it be known that he does not think much of Kinnock's unilateral defence policy.

I AM NEIL KINNOCK SIRE FUTURE LORD OF ALL ENGLAND AND I BRING GOOD TIDINGS REGARDING CRUISE MISSILES

KINNOCK EXPLAINS HIS POSITION TO REAGAN

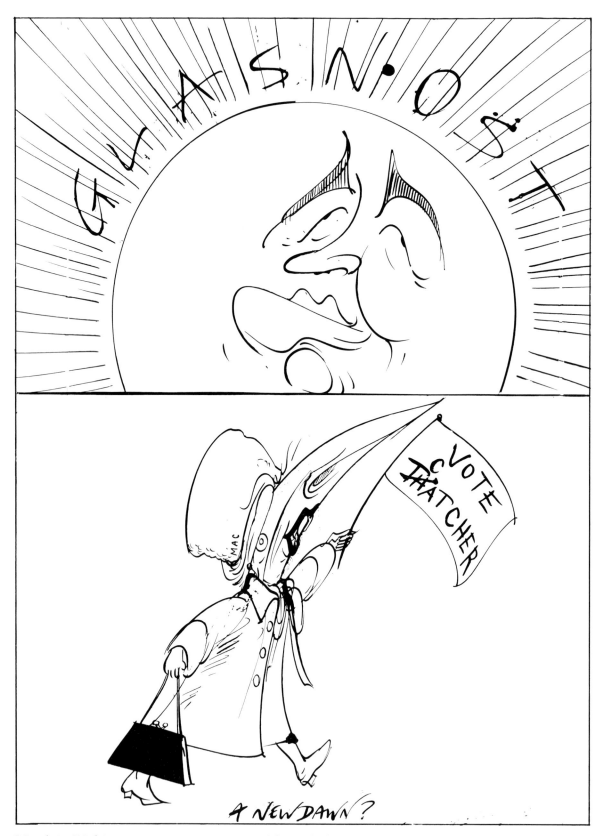

March 29 Wishing to appear an international figure before the election, Mrs Thatcher visits Gorbachev and experiences Glasnost, or openness.

May 10 South Africa. ▶

May 17 The 1987 election fight. Margaret Thatcher, Dr David Owen, Neil Kinnock and David Steel. Margaret Thatcher is still called callous and indifferent to human suffering. Neil Kinnock is generally thought to be the man of the match; he has a good campaign, using the media well, notably a Kennedy-style TV commercial, but the electorate are uncertain about his unilateral disarmament defence programme. Dr David Owen and David Steel are hoping to break the mould of British politics with their Alliance party.

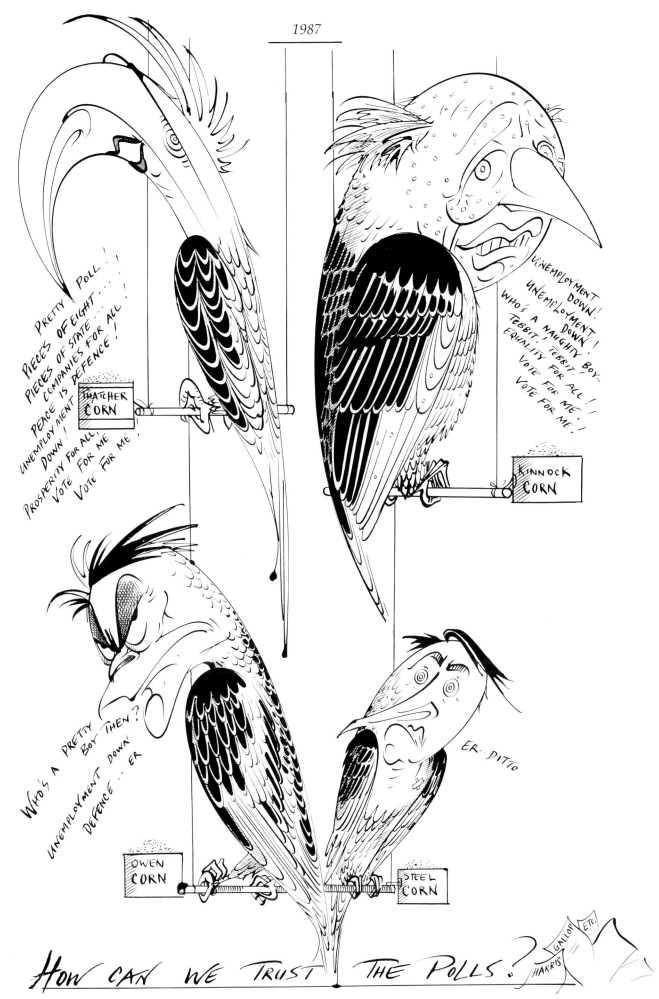

HOW CAN WE TRUST THE POLLS?

May 31 Election to be held on June 11. Great attention is paid to the polls. Have people had enough of Thatcherism?

June 7 The Election is on June 11. Margaret Thatcher, Neil Kinnock and Dr David Owen.

June 14 Mrs Thatcher wins the election by a huge majority. Dr David Owen and the Alliance suffer an election setback. Mr Steel will suggest that the two parties unite in a democratic fusion. Dr Owen sees this as a Liberal attack against the SDP's sovereignty. Her support for private health schemes causes comment.

September 27 The Labour Party.

November 22 Kenneth Baker, Minister of Education, and opposition to the Education Reform Bill. Will a small meritocracy grab the best places while the majority of children miss out? Or will Mr Baker's claim that he offers better choice and standards prove to be true?

THE GREAT DIVIDE

October 11 The Tory Party Conference. The Thatcher era shows no
sign of coming to an end. Mrs Thatcher is based on the current Tory symbol

◄ **June 21** Unemployment figures drop.

June 28 How much did Reagan know about Irangate? Reagan says he knew nothing about Lieutenant-Colonel North and the National Security Council's efforts to keep the Contras alive. He also maintains that the arms he sent to Iran were part of a wide strategic exercise to achieve a working relationship with Iran. Sarah Brightman is at first refused permission to play in the New York production of *The Phantom of the Opera*.

July 12 Lieutenant-Colonel Oliver North and Reagan. North, the scapegoat, is quizzed over Irangate on TV, watched by most of the country. He becomes a star. He admits to telling lies. He admits he would have given the Ayatollah a free trip to Disneyland to get American hostages released. North assumed he had the President's authority and in his testimony names anyone who was anyone in the White House. Knowing exactly what he was doing they took the Ayatollah's money and gave it to the Contras. He shredded the evidence, he does not implicate the President, Ollie-mania sweeps the country. 'We love Ollie,' says a 6-foot high sign in New York. Irangate differs from the Watergate scandal because the President was pushing political rather than party aims.

November 29 Reagan sets up a prestigious meeting with Gorbachev in Washington but Mrs
Thatcher pips him to the post by seeing Gorbachev in England en route. Gorbachev has deliv-
ered his vision of Russia's future in his book 'Perestroika' (or 'Reconstruction').
He says that Russian society is ripe for change - there have been too many official lies.

1988

THE DOVE RETURNS.

NATIONAL HEALTH CARE

HOLE IN THE HEART

January 10 The Hole in the Heart - complaints about the inadequate state of the Health Service. Many are on waiting lists for an interminable length of time.

◀ **January 3** The New Year.

◀◀ **June 5** The Reagan peace dove. Reagan visits Gorbachev in Moscow. Human rights are discussed, the withdrawal from Afghanistan continues, and Cuban troop withdrawals from Angola are to be pressed. Mr Gorbachev wants to concentrate on problems at home.

January 24 Robert MacLennan and David Steel make a terrible mess of launching their new party, the Liberal and Social Democrats. A Liberal and Social Democrat farce: David Steel and Robert Maclennan declare on a Wednesday a set of policies which in a document five days later get absolutely no mention. Prince Edward has recently joined Andrew Lloyd Webber's Really Useful Theatre company. He is renowned for his theatrical interests, including an appearance with other members of the Royal Family in the BBC programme It's a *Knock-Out*.

February 1 Two dead ducks...David Steel, Robert MacLennan. The Liberal and Social Democrats collapse. Dr Owen hovers in the background.

May 15 David Steel resigns

February 14 Valentine Cards:
Mrs Thatcher says we are paying too much in EEC subsidies.
The President of Austria, Kurt Waldheim, refuses to resign despite allegations about his Nazi past.

A VERY RICH MEAL

March 20 Nigel Lawson produces a budget which favours the rich. Top rate of tax to be 40 per cent.

April 3 The Visionary. Prince Charles voices concern over the terrible state of the environment. In 1984 he castigated the planned extension to the National Gallery as a "carbuncle" and in 1987 he said "What have we done to St Pauls? Why has the London skyline been wrecked? and the dome of St Paul's desecrated and lost in a jostling slum of mediocre office buildings."

March 13 Senator Dole and Senator Robertson drop out of the Presidential race. George Bush starts his flight towards the White House.

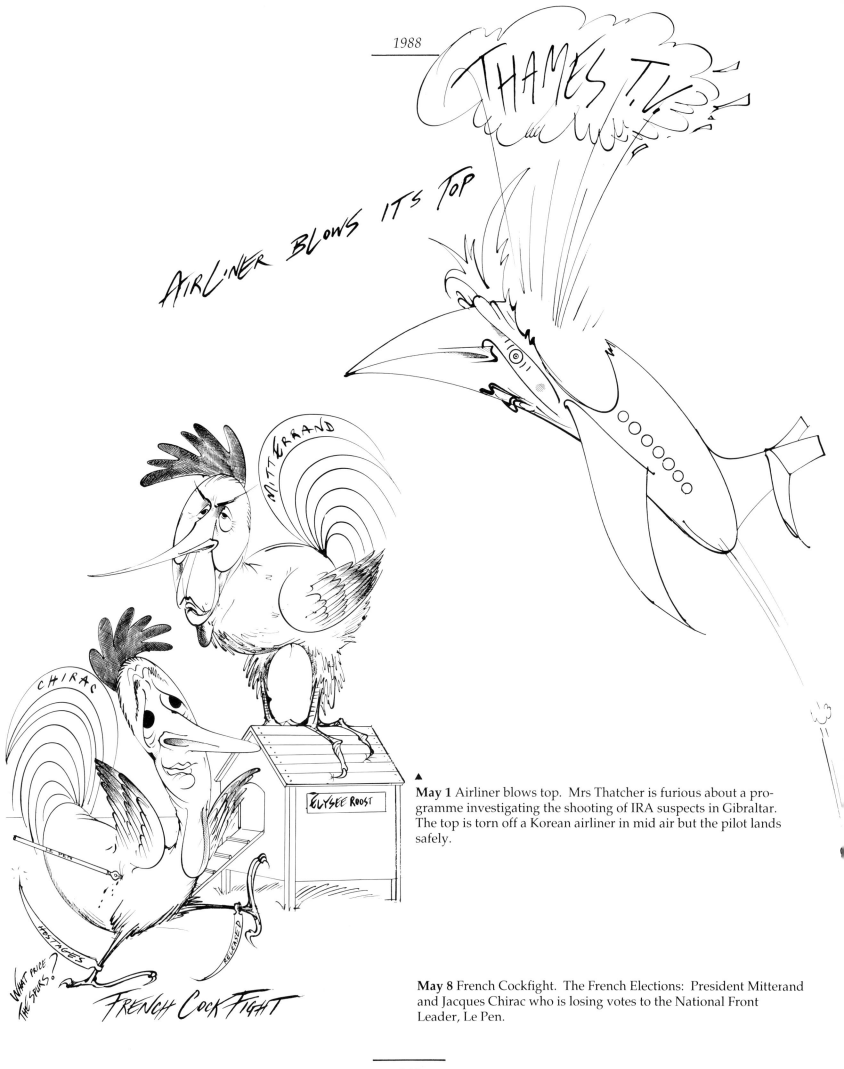

THAMES T.V.

AIRLINER BLOWS ITS TOP

MITTERRAND

CHIRAC

LE PEN

ELYSEE ROOST

HOSTAGES RELEASED

WHAT PRICE THE SPURS?

FRENCH COCK FIGHT

▲

May 1 Airliner blows top. Mrs Thatcher is furious about a programme investigating the shooting of IRA suspects in Gibraltar. The top is torn off a Korean airliner in mid air but the pilot lands safely.

May 8 French Cockfight. The French Elections: President Mitterand and Jacques Chirac who is losing votes to the National Front Leader, Le Pen.

THE STARS AND YOUR SUMMIT

A TRICKY WEEK FOR YOU
A 'FRIEND' MAY BE TOUCHY ON HUMAN RIGHTS
BUT WITH GLASNOST AND PERESTROIKA IN THE
ASCENDANCY — YOU MUST PRESS FOR AN
ARMS DEAL AND A PLACE IN HISTORY.

WATCH OUT FOR TROUBLE WHEN THE
STARS NANCY AND RAISA COLLIDE
IN CLOSE ORBIT !....

NEW BLOOMS IN MOSCOW

May 23 At the Communist party conference in Moscow Gorbachev declares his intention to continue with his liberalisation policy.

◄ **May 29** Gypsy Rose Reagan. Mrs Nancy Reagan is known to consult an astrologer. Reagan heads for the summit in Moscow.

FOR THE LOSS OF A SHOE . . . .

June 26 Norman Willis and the TUC issue an ultimatum to Eric Hammond and his 340,000-strong union, the EEPTU, to cease single union no-strike deals or face expulsion from the TUC.

THE TERRORIST

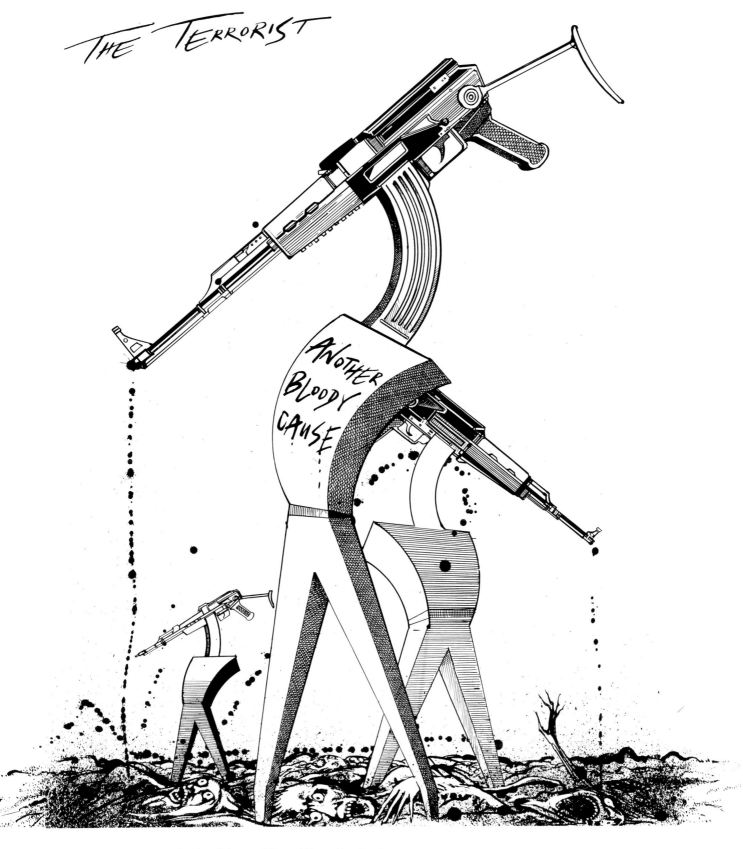

ANOTHER BLOODY CAUSE

July 17 Arab terrorists attack a Greek island ferry, *'City of Poros'* in the Aegean.

THEY'RE OFF!

July 24 Republican George Bush and Democrat Mike Dukakis commence their run towards the White House.

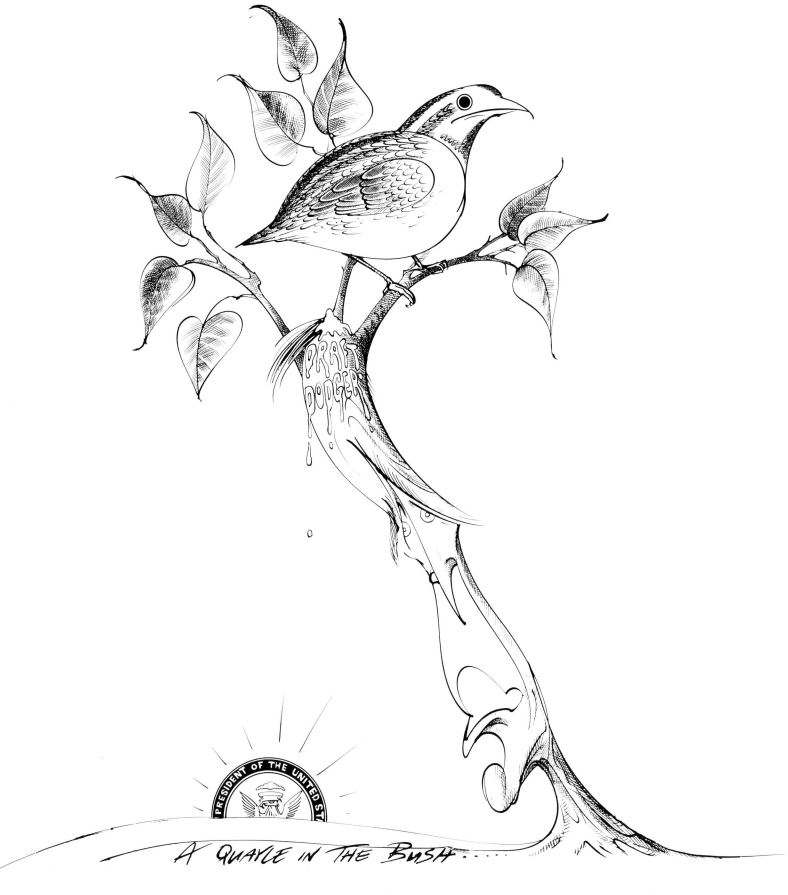

A QUAYLE IN THE BUSH.....

August 21 At the Democratic convention in Texas, Vice President George Bush chooses young, unknown Senator Dan Quayle as his running mate. It is said that Quayle pulled strings to join the National Guard rather than serve in Vietnam; this reflects badly on the Bush/Quayle ticket.

Index

◄ **July 10** An explosion wrecks the North Sea oil platform Piper Alpha and kills 146 men.

I am grateful to Janine and Viv for all their hard work. G.S.